COSMETIC CHEMISTRY FOR DERMATOLOGISTS

By

EMIL G. KLARMANN, Sc.D., D.Sc.(Hon.), Ch.E.

Lecturer, Department of Dermatology
New York University Post-Graduate Medical School
New York City

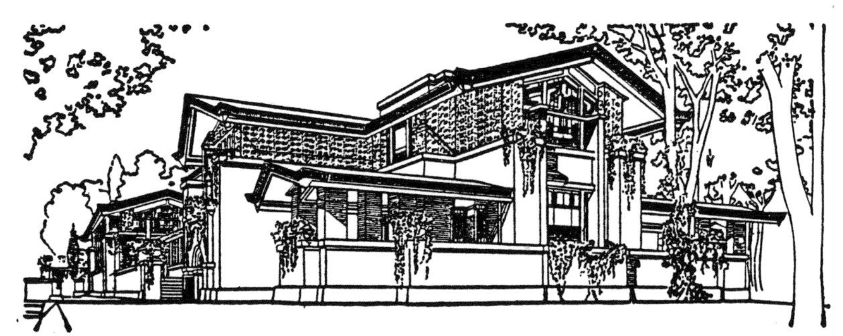

CHARLES C THOMAS • PUBLISHER
Springfield • Illinois • U.S.A.

Published and Distributed Throughout the World by
CHARLES C THOMAS • PUBLISHER
BANNERSTONE HOUSE
301-327 East Lawrence Avenue, Springfield, Illinois, U.S.A.

Library of Congress Catalog Card Number: 62-12048

With THOMAS BOOKS careful attention is given to all details of manufacturing and design. It is the Publisher's desire to present books that are satisfactory as to their physical qualities and artistic possibilities and appropriate for their particular use. THOMAS BOOKS will be true to those laws of quality that assure a good name and good will.

Printed in the United States of America

To Piccina

Forma dei munus: forma quota quaeque superbit?

Pars vestrum tali munere magna caret.

Cura dabit faciem; facies neglecta peribit

Iraliae similis sit licet illa deae.

(Beauty is a gift divine: yet how few can boast of beauty?

Many there are who lack so precious a gift.

But care will provide good looks, while neglect will waste a face

Though it resemble Venus' own.)

OVID, ARS AMATORIA III 103-106.

CONTENTS

COSMETIC CHEMISTRY FOR DERMATOLOGISTS

Chapter 1

INTRODUCTORY REMARKS

THIS SERIES OF LECTURES on "Cosmetic Chemistry for Dermatologists" originated with a review of this subject within the course on "Industrial Dermatoses." Because of the brevity of the presentation imposed by the original framework of this course, a number of participants requested its broadening in order to render greater justice to the position of cosmetics in the dermatological picture.

The treatment of the subject is intended to be such as to provide adequate informational coverage for the dermatologist's purposes, but without the detail which would interest the cosmetic chemist more than the physician. Thus the several formulas given in the text may not always represent the ultimate in technical refinement; however, they are not only workable, but also more directly illustrative of the formulation principles involved, precisely because of their simplicity. Also for purely didactic reasons, the material is often arranged so as to maintain an organic rather than a systematic scheme, as, e.g., when reviewing the initial materials for cosmetics following the discussion of one of the formulas (early in the text) which specifies some of these materials. Among other things, it is the purpose of these lectures to provide the dermatologist with information which would enable him to proceed in a pragmatic manner when confronted with a dermal condition attributed to cosmetic usage.

In this connection it may be remembered that the sales of cosmetics are approaching the two billion dollar mark, a fact which reflects the widespread, if not ubiquitous use of cosmetic preparations. With this as a premise, it should be somewhat surprising to find a comparatively limited interest in cosmetics on the part of physicians, unless it be assumed that the physician, particularly the skin specialist, is attracted more by the diverse skin pathologies than by the comparatively minor and infrequent dermal manifestations of adverse effects of cosmetics. However, this position, albeit justified in some small measure, should call for a modification, firstly because of the enormously widespread usage of cosmetics, and secondly, because the application of some so-called cosmetics often reaches beyond the simple care of the skin surface, affecting certain aspects of skin physiology or pathology.

Of course, none of this has any bearing upon the problem of safety of cosmetics which, as a class, are usually harmless and often beneficial to the skin. Obviously, those few cosmetics which for the sake of their functional utility exhibit some potentially "drastic" qualities (as, e.g., the comparatively alkaline depilatories), may be expected to give rise to untoward skin reactions in a greater number of cases than the great majority of substantially bland and inert preparations. Indeed, it is probably correct to say that the principal factors involved in dermatoses of cosmetic origin are those of hypersensitivity and allergy, although the factor of primary irritation is by no means to be discounted.

In view of the universal appeal of cosmetic preparations and practices, it is not surprising that their history is most fascinating. From the earliest antiquity, through the millennia of recorded history, cosmetics, in one way or another, have been associated with outstanding personages or with important events. However, the history of cosmetics is not a subject for discussion within this lecture series, since it would turn out to be too specialized as well as too extensive, and since ready reference may be made to pertinent literature.

Some general comment may be in order as to the rationale of modern cosmetic formulations. As in the case of drugs, so also in that of cosmetics a profound change has taken place in recent years, with the result that the empirical, sometimes weird concoctions of earlier times have given way to preparations compounded on more rational principles. This is not to say, however, that excursions into the realm of irrationality may not be encountered even today; one still hears, occasionally, of strange or unusual materials being introduced into cosmetic formulas which are more likely to possess virtues originating in the fecund imagination of the promoter than in the recorded observation of some desirable effects upon the skin.

The proper use of properly formulated cosmetics is regarded nowadays as an integral part of good grooming. In addition to cosmetics, in the narrower sense of this term, serving such purpose, there is a variety of others with specialized functions (such as perspiration inhibitors, sunburn preventives, etc.) whose cosmetic end-effects may be preceded by some form of pharmacologic action.

SOME LEGAL ASPECTS OF LABELING AND ADVERTISING OF COSMETICS

As mentioned before, modern cosmetics may be assumed to be innocuous or helpful. While this has not always been the case, today's user is protected against harmful or impure cosmetics by federal and state laws whose cornerstone is the Federal Food, Drug, and Cosmetic Act, in effect since 1938.

The practicing dermatologist should be aware of the existence of this law and of the pertinent regulations. The enforcing agency is the Food and Drug Administration, a division of the U. S. Department of Health, Education and Welfare. Under the provisions of this legislation, the jar, bottle, or other container of a cosmetic preparation is required, among other things, to disclose the name and address of the manufacturer, and the weight or volume of the product. The presence of any ingredient which would render the product injurious under the conditions of use could draw a charge of adulteration, while false or misleading labeling would render it misbranded.

If the effect of the cosmetic is such as to suggest pharmacologic action, the cosmetic becomes additionally a drug; as such, it is subject to the several provisions affecting the labeling of drugs, one of which requires the disclosure on the label of the active ingredient or ingredients responsible for its pharmacologic action. To give an example, a deodorant which is also claimed to check perspiration, would be regarded as both a cosmetic and a drug, the latter by virtue of its capacity to affect a physiological function, *viz.*, the flow of perspiration; accordingly, its label would have to carry the declaration of the particular substance to which the claimed effect is attributed.

The Food, Drug and Cosmetic Act contains other requirements which tend to protect the user of cosmetics. It prohibits the use of unsanitary materials, also the production, packing or storing of cosmetics under conditions which would cause them to become contaminated.

An important section deals with the use of dyes. The Act prohibits the use of any coal-tar dye on eyelashes, on eyebrows or elsewhere in the eye area. The "Color Additives Amendment" which became law recently further tightens the regulatory control over all coloring agents regardless of source, and places them specifically in several categories which determine their fitness for use for particular purposes. A detailed relevant review of the provisions of the Act and of the amendment referred to would be beyond the framework of this presentation.

Cosmetic advertising is subject to regulation by the Federal Trade Commission. The statute enforced by this government agency prohibits dissemination of false information through media such as newspapers and magazines, also radio and television (but not in labeling, the latter being within the purview of the Food, Drug and Cosmetic Act, as indicated above). Claims made in advertising are required to be factual, some allowance being made for the florid language of the average advertisement which should not exceed, however, the limits of "legitimate puffing."

Nevertheless, one may experience, at times, a sense of bewilderment when confronted with advertisements which are so promissory as to be unbelievable or entirely irrational. While this is by no means typical of advertising practice within the cosmetic industry, it is unfortunately true that many objectionable advertisements enjoy a shorter or longer term of existence, usually because of the length of time required by the regulatory agency for their review, and for the subsequent preparation and issuance of a restraining order.

THE COSMETIC "LINE"

With reference to the actual application of cosmetics, the different cosmetic houses advocate their own ideas as to procedure.

Some of them may relate their "lines" of preparations to three fundamental steps, *viz.*, cleansing, conditioning and making-up.

Cleansing is performed with the aid of a soap, or with one of a large variety of cleansing creams or lotions. Conditioning usually involves prolonged application (e.g., overnight) of a suitable preparation whose function it is to help keep the skin smooth and supple. Upon removal of the conditioning agent, there follows often the application of a mild stimulant which doubles sometimes as an aid in removing any residue of the conditioning cream or lotion. Finally, in the process of making-up, face powder (and rouge) may be applied either directly, or over a film of a "foundation" whose function may be twofold: one, continuing "protection" of the skin against exposure (to wind and weather); two, fixation of the powder particles on the skin against loss by movement, by air-currents, etc. Within the recent past a number of tinted "make-up" foundations have come into use whose application may or may not be followed by that of face powder. Finally, lipstick is dabbed on to complete the grooming operation.

Both the users and the formulators of cosmetics are persuaded that all skins are not of the same type, and that there is need, therefore, for special products for each of the three accepted skin types, *viz.*, dry, oily and normal. In the case of some cosmetic houses, this principle may apply to an entire "line" of preparations which, accordingly, may feature special formulations in the cleansing, in the conditioning and in the make-up categories for each of the three skin types. (A corresponding principle applies to dry, oily and normal hair and scalp with specialized preparations available for each of these types.)

While the cosmetic sequence of cleansing, conditioning and making-up is applied at least once daily, a number of other cosmetic preparations may be used more or less regularly. Among the more important are: bath preparations, underarm deodorants, hand and body creams and lotions, nail polish as well as other nail preparations, depilatories, shampoos, waving lotions, hair sprays, colognes and perfumes.

Chapter 2

EMULSIONS AND EMULSIFICATION

MANY COSMETICS are simple mixtures representing aqueous, alcoholic, lipoid or other blends of components. However, numerous cosmetics occur in the form of emulsions; this is why a brief review of the principles underlying the preparation of emulsions is deemed to be desirable.

When olive oil is added to water, the two liquids will form distinct but clear layers, the oil on top, the water at the bottom. Agitation will produce an emulsion, as evidenced by an opacity which forms owing to the disruption of the previously continuous oil phase into tiny globules and their dispersal throughout the mixture. This emulsion is of only temporary duration since on standing an early separation into two layers will take place. However, if a suitable emulsifying agent is added before or during agitation, separation will not take place since a stable emulsion will have been produced.

After this preliminary observation one might consider some pertinent definitions:

An *emulsion* is a system of two immiscible or incompletely miscible liquids, the one being dispersed in the other in the form of discrete globules. The totality of the former represents the internal or dispersed phase, while the surrounding fluid is designated as the external or continuous phase.

While the term "dispersed phase" has been used above in contrast to "continuous phase," it should be noted that the meaning of the term "dispersion" is not limited to emulsions. Thus a *suspension* corresponds to an emulsion except that in the former the dispersed phase consists of solid particles. In a *foam* the dispersed phase is a gas. But in all three systems mentioned, i.e., emulsions, suspensions and foams, the continuous phase is a liquid. Incidentally, an *aerosol* may be regarded as the opposite of a foam since here a gas (air) forms the continuous phase, and a liquid (droplets) the dispersed phase.

Normally, every substance has one or more areas of contact with one or more other substances. Thus, water in a glass is in contact with air at the top, and with glass at the bottom and on the sides. When oil is poured into the container, a new area of contact, a new "interface" is created, *viz.*, that between oil and water, with properties different from those of the other two interfaces. The role which the size of the interface plays in producing an emulsion will be apparent from the following mental experiment:

In a test-tube of exactly one square centimeter in its cross section, one milliliter of oil rests on top of one milliliter of water. The interface between the two liquid phases is now 1 cm^2, and the total volume is 2 ml. Agitating the test-tube causes an emulsion to form whose total volume still is 2 ml. However, the size of the interface has now increased tremendously; assuming an average diameter of 5 microns for each oil droplet, a simple calculation will show that the emulsion will contain over 15 billion oil globules, with a total interface of 12,000 cm^2 or about 1,850 $inches^2$. Globules of 5 microns in diameter are not characteristic of a particularly fine emulsion; if the particle diameter were only 1 micron, there would be 2 trillion globules with an interface of 60,000 cm^2 or about 64 square feet in 2 ml. of the emulsion.

Thus, in an emulsion the interfacial area of the dispersed phase becomes so large as compared to its volume that the surface phenomena acquire a determinative quality.

As is well known, an emulsion of the type under discussion, i.e., produced merely by mechanical agitation, is labile in character; if allowed to stand, it will revert to the simplest two-phase system consisting of two layers through coalescence of the dispersed oil globules. This is due to a force opposing any increase in the surface area of the oil phase above its minimum; this force is known as "interfacial tension."

It is evident that in order to stabilize an emulsion, i.e., prevent its separation into the "oil phase" and "water phase" it will be necessary to lower the interfacial tension between oil and water. This is accomplished with the aid of so-called surface-active materials, or "surfactants" which will act therefore as "emulsifying agents" or "emulsifiers."

A surfactant is characterized by a simultaneous occurrence of hydrophilic and lipophilic groupings in the same molecule. As a result of its oriented adsorption by the oil and water phases, respectively, it modifies and figuratively bridges a gap of dissimilarity between them.

Emulsifiers may be grouped in two main categories, *viz.,* ionic and non-ionic. The former may be either anionic or cationic; both dissociate in water into two electrically charged parts. Under the same conditions, the non-ionic emulsifiers do not "split" into two portions carrying opposite electrical charges.

Soap furnishes an example of an anionic surfactant. As a salt of an aliphatic acid of high molecular weight it dissociates according to the following equation:

$$R.COOM \rightleftharpoons R.CO\overset{-}{O}\ldots\overset{+}{M}$$

where R is a long hydrocarbon chain and M could be sodium, potassium, ammonium, an organic ammonium derivative, or the like.

Emulsions based upon oil and water may be either of the "oil-in-water" (O/W), or of the "water-in-oil" (W/O) type. In the former, the water forms the "continuous" phase, and the oil is in the "dispersed" phase; in the latter the oil makes up the continuous phase, the water the dispersed phase. With the aid of suitable soaps, either type of emulsion can be produced; and the same is true of the anionic surface active salts of high-molecular alkyl, aryl and alkaryl sulfonates and sulfates. The following formulas apply to sodium dodecyl (or lauryl) sulfate (I), and to sodium benzene sulfonate (II), respectively (see next page).

It may be added, for the sake of completeness, that soap "solutions" which are stable at an alkaline pH, break down if an attempt is made to render the solutions neutral or acid. By contrast, the alkyl and aryl sulfates and sulfonates tolerate appreciable degrees

I $$[CH_3(CH_2)_{10}CH_2O-\overset{O}{\underset{O}{\overset{\|}{\underset{\|}{S}}}}-\bar{O}]\ldots\overset{+}{Na}$$

II $$[C_6H_5\overset{O}{\underset{O}{\overset{\|}{\underset{\|}{S}}}}-\bar{O}]\ldots\overset{+}{Na}$$

of acidity of media in which they are dissolved; hence they can be employed in the production of emulsions exhibiting an acid reaction.

Cationic surfactants also comprise several types. Thus a long chain alkyl amine (or rather ammonium) salt would be the cationic counterpart of the anionic soap, as exemplified below by tetradecyl ammonium chloride (I) and sodium myristate (II), respectively:

I $$(C_{14}H_{29})\overset{+}{N}H_3\ldots\overset{-}{Cl}$$

II $$(C_{14}H_{27}O_2)^{-}\ldots\overset{+}{Na}$$

More important cationics are the quaternary ammonium salts ("quats") answering the following general formula:

$$\left[\begin{array}{c} R_1 \\ | \\ R_4-N-R_2 \\ | \\ R_3 \end{array}\right]^{+}\ldots\bar{X}$$

in which R_1 is a long chain hydrocarbon radical, while R_2, R_3, and R_4 represent shorter radicals such as methyl, benzyl, etc.; X is a salt-forming anion, such as chloride, sulfate, acetate and the like. Examples are benzalkonium chloride (i.e., dodecyl benzyl dimethyl ammonium chloride) (I), and cetyl pyridinium chloride (II):

$$\left[(C_{12}H_{25})-\underset{CH_3}{\overset{CH_3}{\underset{|}{\overset{|}{N}}}}-CH_2C_6H_5\right]^{+}\cdots Cl^{-}$$

I

$$\left[C_5H_5N-CH_2(CH_2)_{14}CH_3\right]^{+}\cdots Cl^{-}$$

II

Incidentally, the simple alkyl ammonium salts are sensitive to pH changes toward alkalinity causing them to break down and separate. By contrast, the quaternary ammonium salts are substantially stable at both an acid and an alkaline pH.

In comparing the anionic and the cationic surfactants it will be noted that it is the ion with the high "molecular weight" which exhibits an "oil-soluble" or "lipophilic" character; this would be the anion in the case of a soap or an alkyl sulfate, and the cation in the case of a quaternary ammonium salt. The "hydrophilic" ions are of light weight in both instances (e.g., sodium in the case of a soap, and chlorine in the case of a "quat"). The substantial difference in the weights of the two oppositely charged ions characterizes, among other things, the ionic (i.e., anionic and cationic) surfactants.

In contrast to an anionic and cationic surfactant, a non-ionic surfactant does not dissociate electrolytically or otherwise. It, too, is characterized by the simultaneous occurrence of a hydrophilic and a lipophilic group in the same molecule. As in the case of the ionic surfactants, the lipophilic quality is contributed here primarily by a hydrocarbon chain of adequate length, while the hydrophilic quality depends chiefly upon a cumulation of hydroxyl groups or ether linkages, or both, originating, e.g., with a polyhydric alcohol (polyol) or a polyoxyethylene compound.

Thus a simple example of a non-ionic surfactant would be furnished by a monoester of glycerol, e.g., glyceryl monostearate:

$$\begin{array}{l} CH_2O.CO.C_{17}H_{35} \\ | \\ CHOH \\ | \\ CH_2OH \end{array}$$

Here the $C_{17}H_{35}$ hydrocarbon portion of the stearyl group represents the lipophilic entity while the carboxyglyceryl portion is of hydrophilic character. Similar in character, but more efficient in emulsifying action are the polyoxyethylene fatty acid esters obtained by condensation of fatty acids with ethylene oxide according to the general scheme:

$$R.COOH + \underset{\diagdown O \diagup}{H_2C-CH_2} \rightarrow R.COO.CH_2CH_2OH;$$

$$+n\ \underset{\diagdown O \diagup}{H_2C-CH_2} \rightarrow R.COO.CH_2CH_2\text{-}O\text{-}(CH_2CH_2\text{-}O\text{-})_{n-2}CH_2CH_2OH$$

in which again the aliphatic hydrocarbon portion of the acyl group supplies the lipophilic quality while the polyoxyethylene chain with the hydroxyl group at its open end plus the carboxy portion (from the acyl radical) constitute the hydrophilic portion. A comparable emulsifying performance should be expected of a polyoxyethylene fatty *ether* (obtained by the condensation of an alcohol with ethylene oxide):

$$R.COH + n\ \underset{\diagdown O \diagup}{H_2C-CH_2} \rightarrow R.COCH_2CH_2\text{-}O\text{-}(CH_2CH_2\text{-}O\text{-})_{n-2}CH_2CH_2OH$$

It is noteworthy that the ether linkage would tend to make such a compound resistant to hydrolysis by alkalis and acids within pH ranges which could be destructive to polyoxyethylene *esters*.

Another important group of non-ionic surfactants is derived from the anhydrides of certain hexahydric alcohols (hexitols), such as sorbitol. The latter yields sorbitan (a hexitan), or sorbide (a hexide), by losing one or two molecules of water, respectively. Partial esterification with a fatty acid (such as lauric, palmitic, stearic or oleic) produces a surfactant of the "Span" category, as shown by the following equations:

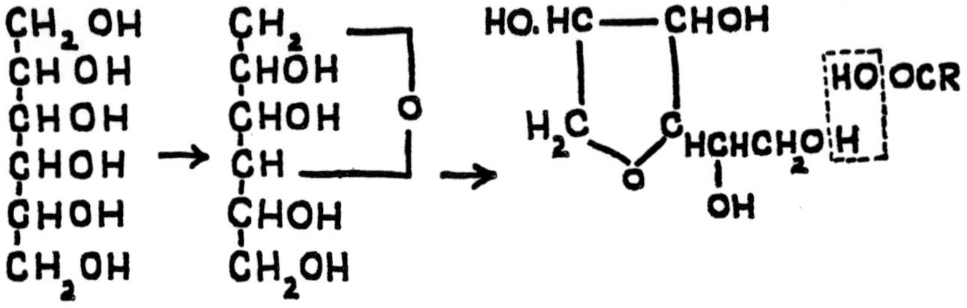

CH_2OH
$CHOH$
$CHOH$
$CHOH$ →
$CHOH$
CH_2OH

CH_2 —┐
$CHOH$ │
$CHOH$ O
CH ——┘ →
$CHOH$
CH_2OH

HO.HC — CHOH
H_2C —O— $CHCHCH_2OH$ + HOOCR
OH

Additional substitution of the available, i.e., non-esterified hydroxyl groups of the hexitans and hexides by polyoxyethylene yields the "Tween" types of surfactants, as shown below:

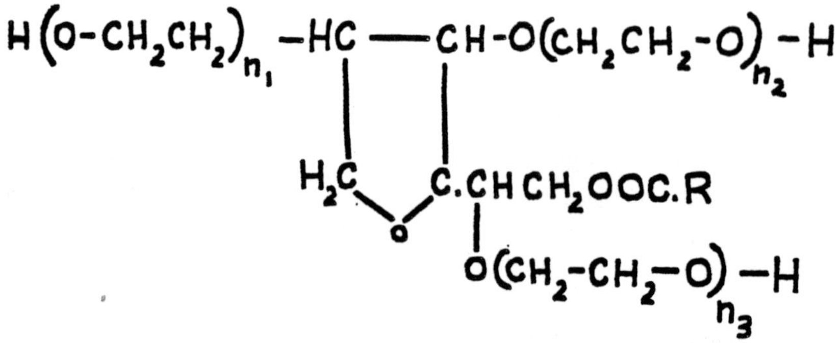

$H(O-CH_2CH_2)_{n_1}-HC$ — $CH-O(CH_2CH_2-O)_{n_2}-H$
H_2C —O— $C.CHCH_2OOC.R$
$O(CH_2-CH_2-O)_{n_3}-H$

The alkylolimids constitute yet another group of surface active agents. They are produced by the condensation of fatty acids with di-alkyol amines, as shown on the following page.

Amphoteric surfactants (produced e.g., by condensation of primary amines with α,β-unsaturated or α-halo acids) are character-

$$R.COOH + HN\begin{matrix} \diagup C_2H_4OH \\ \diagdown C_2H_4OH \end{matrix} \rightarrow R.CON\begin{matrix} \diagup C_2H_4OH \\ \diagdown C_2H_4OH \end{matrix}$$

ized by a stability in both acid and alkaline media, often exhibiting different properties at one and at the other end of the pH scale, respectively. The following sample equation illustrates the condensation of a primary amine with acrylic acid:

$$R.NH_2 + CH_2 = CHCOOH \rightarrow R.\overset{+}{N}H_2CH_2CH_2COO^-$$

$$\text{or} \quad R.NH\begin{matrix} \diagup CH_2CH_2CO\bar{O} \\ \diagdown CH_2CH_2COOH \end{matrix}$$

For the sake of completeness, some reference should be made here to the class of hydrophilic colloids which can act not only as thickeners, but also as emulsifying agents. Among the products of natural origin are gums (such as karaya, tragacanth, acacia), carbohydrates (such as starches and dextrins), proteins (such as casein, gelatin) and others; among the modified natural products are the alginates (from kelp and sea weed), and the cellulose ethers (such as methyl cellulose, carboxy methyl cellulose).

A somewhat special position is occupied by the phospholipids of natural origin, such as lecithin and cephalin. In contrast to true fats which are triglycerides (i.e., with all three hydroxyl groups of glycerol esterified by fatty acids), the phospholipids contain two fatty acids groups in an ester bond with glycerol, while the third hydroxyl group of glycerol is esterified with phosphoric acid which, in turn, carries a choline or aminoethyl alcohol group. The formula on page 16 illustrates the phospholipid, lecithin.

While true fats are entirely lipophilic (owing to the absence in their molecule of any free hydroxyl groups), the cholin substituted phosphoric acid in lecithin imparts to the molecule a measure of hydrophilic quality, thereby permitting it to act as a moderately ef-

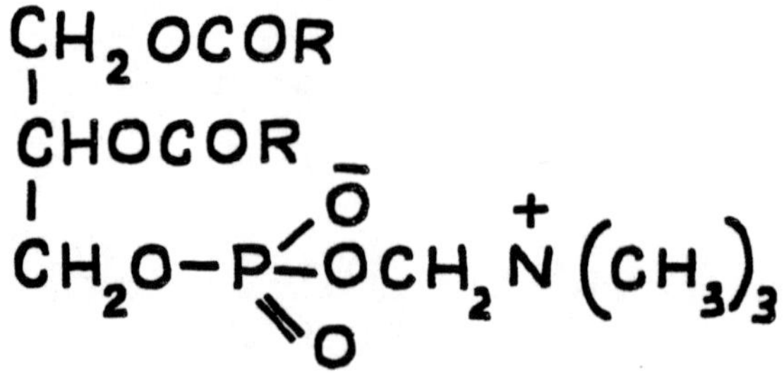

$$
\begin{array}{l}
CH_2OCOR \\
| \\
CHOCOR \\
| \qquad\qquad\quad \bar{O} \\
CH_2O-P(\!=\!O)(-O^-)-OCH_2\overset{+}{N}(CH_3)_3
\end{array}
$$

ficient emulsifying agent for preparations of the O/W type.

Finally, certain insoluble solids can perform as emulsifiers if present in a state of very fine dispersion. By way of examples, silica and bentonite exhibit a kind of hydrophilic character (being readily wetted by water), while carbon black and graphite appear more lipophilic (being more easily wetted by oil).

Oil-in-water emulsions prepared with the aid of ionic emulsifiers are better conductors of electricity than corresponding water-in-oil emulsions. In fact, this is one way of distinguishing between these two emulsion types. Another method is to test for dispersibility; thus, if addition to water of a few drops of an emulsion causes ready dispersion, the emulsion is of the O/W type, the external phase being miscible with water.

Yet another simple method of distinguishing the two emulsion types depends upon the addition of suitable dyes; thus, with an oil soluble dye rapid coloration will take place only in the case of a W/O emulsion, since its external phase is oil; with a water soluble dye, coloration would occur promptly in the case of an O/W emulsion type.

Chapter 3

CLEANSING AGENTS

DETERGENTS (SOAP AND SHAMPOO)

THE SKIN CLEANSER *par excellence* is soap. Although water alone exhibits a fair degree of cleansing action, particularly with respect to water soluble impurities, soap additionally emulsifies the oily soil for easy removal by subsequent rinsing. Since solid particles of grime and of make-up are trapped and held on the skin either by adventitious oiliness or by autochthonous sebum, or by both, the removal from the skin of such soil is made possible by emulsification and rinsing.

While oily soil can be removed also by means of suitable solvents (e.g., benzene or kerosene) their routine use for cleansing is undesirable because they tend to "defat" the skin to a far greater extent than the normal skin would tolerate. On the other hand, certain oil solvents, such as refined liquid petrolatum, are prescribed for occasional use where soap-and-water cleansing may have been found to produce an adverse effect upon the skin.

Toilet soaps are not classifiable as cosmetics in the "legal" sense of this term; they are specifically exempted from any regulatory application of the cosmetic section of the Federal Food, Drug and Cosmetic Act.

Most toilet soaps are compounded carefully so as to avoid the presence of any unreacted fats (fatty acids) or free alkali. However, in contact with water every soap generates an alkaline reaction (of moderate intensity), owing to hydrolysis; this takes place according to the following equation (applying to sodium oleate):

$$C_{17}H_{33}COONa + H_2O \rightleftharpoons C_{17}H_{33}COOH + NaOH$$

Hydrolysis with concomitant pH over 7 is a general characteristic of alkali salts of weakly dissociating acids; thus the tendency of the acid anion to reconstitute the undissociated acid by combining with the hydrogen ion of water, creates an excess of hydroxyl ions and thereby an alkaline reaction. It was found that the normal acidity of the skin is shifted temporarily towards alkaline by washing with soap, but that it returns to normal within a period of time which may vary from one to several hours; however, during this period of a changed pH the skin's antimicrobial defense action appears to be impaired.

The mode of action of soaps and other detergents is quite complex and not entirely clarified in all its aspects. However, the following individual mechanisms appear to be involved in the cleansing process:

1. Lowering of the surface tension of water, which permits a more intimate contact between the detergent solution and the skin.
2. Emulsification of any lipoid matter present on the skin.
3. Wetting and suspension in the detergent solution of water insoluble particles of grime.
4. Mechanical action in loosening the soil from the surface to be cleansed.
5. Removal by rinsing of the detergent solution carrying the emulsified lipoid matter and suspended grime.

Normal, healthy skin tolerates the regular and frequent use of correctly formulated soaps and other detergents. Their desirable cleansing action involves the removal of desquamating keratin, cutaneous secretions, pathogenic microorganisms, cellular debris, air-borne pollutants and a number of potentially harmful contactants of environmental origin. Moreover, soaps and detergents have a record of effectiveness in the prophylaxis as well as in the symptomatic therapy of certain dermatoses, such as acne and seborrhea.

Nevertheless, eczema attributed to the use of soap is by no means uncommon. While it has been known for some time that repeated or prolonged immersion in soap solutions may bring about a superficial cutaneous alteration, some investigators ascribed this effect to the penetration into the epidermis of an irritant fatty acid (such as lauric acid) liberated from the soap at the pH of the cutaneous surface.

Pathological skin may respond more acutely to the alkaline reaction of the soap solution, or to some component of the soap or of the fat from which the soap has been produced. In this case a suitable "soapless" cleanser may be indicated, employing a sulfonated fatty oil, or some synthetic anionic detergent with a low irritation potential. Such detergents may be formulated so as to yield solutions within the neutral-to-acid range for the sake of a better approximation to the skin's normal reaction.

Actually, synthetic anionic detergents (alkyl sulfates and alkyl benzene sulfonates) do not normally penetrate the intact skin. However, from a buffered *sodium laurate* solution penetration occurs only if its pH is below 8.5 or above 10.5, but not within the range of 8.5 to 10.5. Skin penetration at the lower pH is attributed to a better lipid solubility, while penetration at the higher pH is due to structural alteration. Since a buffered sodium laurate solution produces an erythema at pH 7.5, but not at 9.5, it may be necessary to reconsider the role heretofore ascribed to free fatty acids or to free alkali as erythemogenic factors.

There exists evidence to the effect that allergic sensitization by household soaps and synthetic detergents occurs but rarely; however, both can induce pathological alterations of the skin, or aggravate certain existing dermatoses (e.g., ichthyosis, xerosis, senile skin). Such untoward reactions appear to be favored by a low environmental humidity or temperature, or both, since the former counteracts adequate keratin hydration, while the latter has an adverse effect upon cutaneous circulation thereby lowering the protective activity of the sebaceous and the sweat glands.

Special skin cleansers based upon organic sulfates or sulfonates are sometimes combined with emollients, such as liquid petrolatum, lanolin and the like; the purpose of these additives is to counteract "drying" of the skin by prolonged exposure to uncombined soaps or detergents which tend to emulsify and remove the autochthonous skin lipids. Incidentally, a similar effect is expected from the use of so-called "superfatted" soaps which may contain some unsaponified fat (or unreacted fatty acids), or extraneous matter of the type of lanolin, "cold cream," etc. There is no good reason to believe, however, that the action on the skin of a superfatted soap will be substantially different from that of the corresponding neutral soap—primarily because the emulsifying action of the soap itself would militate against the deposition upon, and retention by the skin of any significant quantity of the superfatting ingredients; as will be seen later, remedial lubrication of the skin is achieved more easily and more effectively by direct application to the dry skin of a suitable emollient cream or lotion.

In cases of verified intolerance to either soap or synthetic detergents, a demulcent application of an aqueous dispersion of starch, oatmeal and the like may be found useful, at least as a temporary expedient.

The so-called "detergent bars" which have come into use in the comparatively recent past are made from closely guarded formulas. They may represent combinations of synthetic detergents with soaps, or they may contain one or more synthetic surfactants alone, usually combined with suitable fillers such as gums, starches, sodium alginate, carboxymethyl cellulose, and the like. The following formula illustrates a (patented) composition of an all-purpose detergent bar in which the filler is the insoluble calcium stearate, while the other three components are from the class of anionic surfactants:

Detergent Bar

	Per Cent
Calcium stearate	70.0
Sodium dodecylbenzene sulfonate	15.0
Sodium diisopropyl naphthalene sulfonate	7.5
Sodium diamylsulfosuccinate	7.5

A somewhat special position is held by the *"deodorant soap."* This type of soap may be regarded as an outgrowth of the "degerming" soap (often referred to incorrectly as "germicidal" soap) introduced originally into surgical routine with the view to lowering the bacterial count on the hands of operating room personnel, and thus reducing the risk of surgical wound infection. The cosmetic aspect of such soap arises from the fact that the same mechanism which counteracts infection also controls body odor of perspiratory origin. As will be shown elsewhere ("Antiperspirants and Deodorants"), this odor is due predominantly to bacterial decomposition of organic matter in perspiration, notably of the apocrine variety, with formation of malodorous end products.

The deodorant soap usually contains one of a number of suitable antibacterial agents (hexachlorophene, bithionol) to be retained by the skin (following routine use, uninterrupted by the use of any non-medicated soap) in an amount sufficient to suppress the activity and proliferation of those dermal microorganisms which would attack and decompose the organic matter carried by perspiration.

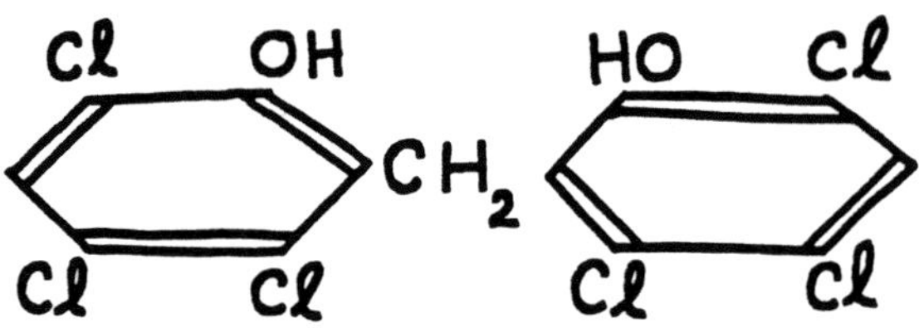

I

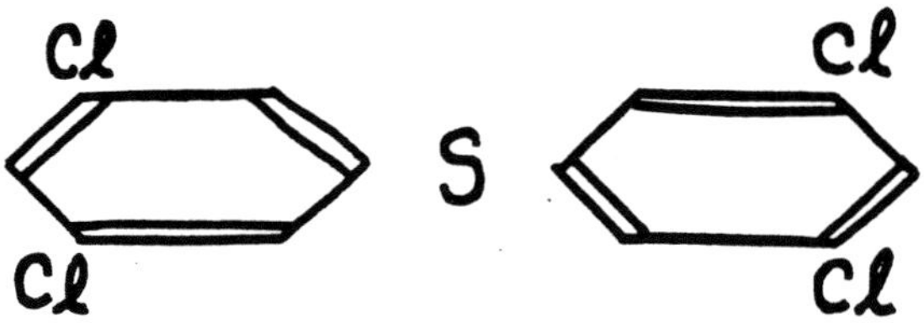

II

While hexachlorophene (I) and bithionol (II) are classified as phenol derivatives, fitness for use in deodorant ("degerming") soaps is not an exclusive characteristic of this class of compounds. Thus tetramethylthiuram disulfide (TMTD), with the formula:

$$(CH_3)N\overset{\overset{S}{\|}}{C}S.S\overset{\overset{S}{\|}}{C}N(CH_3)_2$$

and 3,4,4′-trichlorocarbanilide (TCC) with the formula:

impart effective deodorant (and degerming) action to toilet soap, to mention but two non-phenolic soap additives of current usage. Synergistic potentiation of antibacterial action is claimed for a combination of hexachlorophene with TCC.

A cleansing agent for the hair (and scalp) is designated as a *"shampoo."* While ordinary cake soap could be (and is being) used for this purpose, the modern shampoo is compounded specially to produce a satisfactory effect with respect not only to its cleaning action, but also to its capacity for leaving the hair in a lustrous and manageable condition.

Many different types of shampoos are available. The cleansing principle may be a soap, a soapless detergent, or a combination of both. In appearance, the shampoo may represent a transparent liquid, or a cream (in paste or liquid form). Often special formulas are produced for normal, dry and oily hair. Many shampoos contain different additives, such as egg powder, lanolin, herbal extracts, etc., each credited with a particular beneficial function.

In hard water regions, shampoos based upon soapless detergents merit preference, since the insoluble soap curd precipitated by calcium and magnesium bicarbonates (constituting the "hardness" of the water) can dull the appearance of the hair and cause it to "mat."

In preparing a soap type shampoo, the mixture of fatty oils, usually consisting of coconut and olive oils, is saponified with potassium hydroxide to yield a soft soap "solution." One can also employ finished neutral potassium soap and prepare a shampoo, e.g., according to the following formula:

Soap Shampoo

	Per Cent
Potassium coconut oil soap	25.0
Potassium olive oil soap	5.0
Alcohol	15.0
Glycerol	5.0
Water	50.0

The soap ingredient of a shampoo may be produced also by the neutralization of one or more fatty acids which are available as such.

The lathering effect of a soap depends, among other things, upon the chain length of its fatty acid component. Coconut oil soap which contains the salts of lauric (C_{12}) and myristic (C_{14}) acids is distinguished by excellent lathering action. However, there are indications that used by itself, this type of soap is drying to the hair, also irritating to the scalp, particularly in routine usage. Thus, one purpose of blending coconut oil with other fatty oils (such as olive oil or palm oil) is to minimize these disadvantages. Incidentally, the irritant action referred to is aggravated by the salts of the short-chain caprylic (C_8) and capric (C_{10}) acids, both of which are present among the fatty acids of coconut oil.

In order to improve the performance of soap shampoos in hard water, so-called "sequestering" agents are added. Among the more important is ethylene diamine tetraacetic acid (EDTA) which deprives the calcium and magnesium ions of their ion status by "chelation," thereby rendering them unavailable for precipitation of the insoluble calcium and magnesium soaps.

Isolated fatty acids can be neutralized with triethanolamine instead of sodium or potassium hydroxide. These triethanolammonium salts are soaps of lower alkalinity (as formed by hydrolysis), than the corresponding sodium or potassium salts. Following is an illustrative formula of a "triethanolamine shampoo":

Soap Shampoo

	Per Cent
Coconut oil fatty acids	20.0
Oleic acid	27.5
Triethanolamine	27.5
Propylene glycol	25.0

Soapless shampoos are formulated, as a rule, with anionic surfactants, such as sodium or triethanolamine lauryl (dodecyl) sulfate. The stronger "defatting" action of such shampoos can be modified with the aid of suitable additives, e.g., the mono- or diethanol amids of fatty acids. Following is an illustrative example of a soapless shampoo:

Soapless Shampoo

	Per Cent
Triethanolamine dodecyl sulfate	40.0
Ethanolamid of dodecanoic (lauric) acid	15.0
Water	45.0

Yet another class of shampoos utilizes sulfonated (or sulfated) fatty oils, such as sulfated olive oil or "turkey red oil," the latter being a (neutralized) sulfated castor oil.

While providing effective cleansing action these shampoos do not lather too well.

In the recent past, literally hundreds of new surfactants have been made available by chemical synthesis. Some of them were employed in shampoo formulation, sometimes without prior inquiry as to any inherent capacity for eye irritation. As a result, difficulties arose particularly with some preparations based upon cationic surfactants (quarternary ammonium compounds) which were found to be capable of causing severe eye irritation, occasionally culminating with irreversible corneal opacity; it should be noted, in this connection, that such compounds do not usually cause eye sting, thus providing no warning against the hazard of a severe injury to the eye. Comparatively stingless and non-irritant shampoos ("baby shampoos") may be formulated with selected representatives from the class of amphoteric surfactants.

CLEANSING CREAMS

One of the oldest, and still one of the most popular cosmetic cleansers, is the so-called *cold cream;* in addition to its "classical" formula, there are numerous modifications both in hydrous ointment and in liquid emulsion forms.

The original formula of cold cream has been attributed to Galen. Essentially, ordinary cold cream is a W/O type of emulsion which in one of its simplest forms may be made from beeswax, mineral oil, borax and water, e.g., in the following proportions:

Cold Cream

	Per Cent
Beeswax	16.0
Mineral oil	50.0
Borax	1.0
Water	33.0

Although it is not intended hereafter to give the methods of preparation of the different formulas, the procedure of making this cold cream is given below in some detail as an illustration of the basic principle which applies to the preparation of emulsions in general, *viz.*:

1. Combine the "lipoid" ingredients, beeswax and mineral oil,

and heat to 70°C until a clear liquid results.

2. In a separate container dissolve borax in water and heat to 70°C.

3. While stirring vigorously, add the borax solution to the melted beeswax-mineral oil melt. When the temperature has dropped to 42°C pour into jars.

(As a rule about 0.5 per cent of a perfume is stirred into the melt at 45°C.)

The reason why the above formula yields an emulsion is that in the course of its production an emulsifying agent is generated *in situ* owing to a reaction between borax and the free fatty acids of beeswax. (While beeswax is essentially of a monoester character, it also contains some free fatty acids, i.e., in non-esterified form.) Although all of the latter are not of the same molecular weight, the following illustrative reaction is based upon the constituent hexacosanoic acid (i.e., aliphatic fatty acid with 26 carbons), "cerotic acid":

$$C_{25}H_{51}COOH + Na_2B_4O_7 = C_{25}H_{51}COONa + H_3BO_3 + H_2O$$

The "sodium cerotate" thus formed has emulsifying action, being the alkali salt of a high-molecular fatty acid and thereby resembling a soap which is an emulsifier, as outlined before.

Cold creams are efficient skin cleansers. Their cleansing action may be assumed to depend upon a combination of two effects. First, the "lipoid" portion of the cold cream "dissolves" the sebum and loosens the desquamated epithelial keratin, also the particles of soil and make-up from their adhesive contact with the skin; next, the emulsifying effect takes over for an easier removal of suspended autochthonous as well as extraneous matter by mechanical means, such as cleansing tissue applied with moderate friction. Thus the action of a cold cream may be said to combine to some extent the effect of a lipoid solvent with that of a detergent.

A cold cream prepared by the beeswax-borax emulsifying principle will display an alkaline reaction (albeit of a mild degree), owing to the hydrolysis of "sodium cerotate." This alkalinity would be comparable to (or be weaker than) that of a soap solution; it is readily tolerated by a normal skin. Since cold cream (like soap) is not left on the skin, but is removed soon after application, the normal physiological pH is re-established within a short period of time. However, where a special dermatological problem may require complete non-interference with the skin's physiological pH, it would not be feasible to satisfy such a requirement by adjusting the pH of the cold cream to the normally acid dermal pH through the addition of an acidic substance, as this would immediately decompose the "cerotate" with liberation of "cerotic acid," thereby causing the emulsion system to "break." However, with the aid of a suitable non-ionic emulsifier it is possible to replace "sodium cerotate", and thus to obtain a cold cream with a neutral reaction; if desired, an acid reacting cream could be produced by the addition of a suitable acidic substance. A simple cold cream type of formula, *without beeswax and borax,* might show the following composition:

Cold Cream

	Per Cent
Mineral oil	22.5
Petrolatum	32.5
Paraffin	10.0
Sorbitan sesquioleate	5.0
Water	30.0

In preparing this type of emulsion, the first five ingredients are melted together and heated to 70°C, whereupon the water (previously warmed to 70°C) is added to the melt gradually with stirring. Sometimes supplementary homogenization (at 55 to 60°C) is carried out prior to filling, for the sake of perfect smoothness and uniformity.

The above formulas permit of a wide variety of modifications and variations. Thus to render a cream more appropriate for dry skin, it may be modified by the addition of vegetable oil, of lanolin, and the like, to the lipoid phase, or by adding a humectant such as glycerol, propylene glycol or sorbitol to the aqueous phase, or both. The purpose of these additions is not primarily one of producing an emollient effect, since in normal usage the cleansing cream or lotion does not remain in contact with the skin for a sufficiently long period of time; rather, the intent is to counteract any extensive "defatting" of a dry skin by too thorough a cleansing action, as this might give rise to some undesirable sequelae of exacerbation of an existing dryness.

Emulsified cleansing preparations occur in a variety of cream consistencies as well as in the form of liquids of different viscosities. Following is a sample formula of a liquid cleansing emulsion:

Liquid Cleansing Emulsion

	Per Cent
Mineral oil	45.0
Diglycol laurate	15.0
Water	40.0

The "diglycol laurate" which acts as a non-ionic emulsifying agent is actually diethylene glycol monolaurate, i.e. a mono-ester of a dihydric alcohol: $C_{11}H_{23}COOCH_2CH_2OCH_2CH_2OH$, with a lipophilic and a hydrophilic group in its molecule.

The oily skin, with its abundance of sebaceous secretion, calls for cleansing action directed toward removal of oiliness. This can be achieved by efficient emulsification with soap or with another suitable detergent agent (e.g., sulfonated olive oil, triethanolamine lauryl sulfate, etc.), as outlined before; it is being done also with the aid of special cosmetic cleansing "creams" of the "liquefying" type. A simple formula of a so-called liquefying cleansing cream might consist of the following ingredients of mineral (paraffinic) origin:

Liquefying Cleansing Cream

	Per Cent
Mineral oil	65.0
Paraffin	20.0
Petrolatum	15.0

This preparation is obtained by melting its components together, and allowing the melt to solidify in jars. Applied to the warm skin it liquefies to a viscous fluid which dissolves the oily coating of the skin for easy removal with soft paper tissue or a cloth towel. Parenthetically, there is some evidence in support of the argument that in contrast to lanolin or the true fats and oils (triglycerides), the application of mineral oil does not aggravate an existing oily skin condition.

Chapter 4

CONDITIONING PREPARATIONS

THE CREAMS AND LOTIONS in this not too well defined group of preparations are intended to furnish lubricant, emollient or humectant action, and preferably a combination of any two or of all three effects, with the view to promoting skin smoothness, and relieving dryness and roughness. In contrast to cleansing cosmetics which are left on the skin for only short periods of time, the preparations of this group remain in contact with the skin for longer periods, e.g., over night.

It has been known for some time that the natural lipid film present upon the skin surface does not suffice to prevent water loss from the horny layer. Moreover, a barrier which is located between the cornified epithelium and the underlying moist tissue usually prevents complete replacement from this tissue of the water lost by the *stratum corneum* through evaporation. Thus, when the ambient relative humidity drops to low levels (e.g., during the winter months), the *stratum corneum* may dry out to the extent of becoming brittle and fragile. Less severe atmospheric conditions may produce skin dryness, the degree of which will vary with the individual.

Prior to the advent of federal and state regulations of labeling and advertising, preparations of the type belonging in the category of skin conditioners were being referred to variously as "skin foods," "nourishing creams," etc. Such and similar designations had to be abandoned since, of course, the skin cannot be "nourished" from the outside by the application of cosmetic creams or lotions, depending instead for its nourishment upon circulation like any other organ of the body; of course, the lifeless corneous layer of the skin cannot participate in this process. However, a properly formulated conditioning cream might be expected to have a beneficial action upon the skin in protecting it against the effects of "weathering" (such as irritation, chapping, etc.), by making the horny layer supple and pliable instead of leaving it dry and brittle. This result is achieved primarily through a reduction of the water loss from the skin, usually by means of a combination of several effects, *viz.*, an "occlusive" lipid film deposited upon the skin as the non-volatile residue of the cream or lotion, the "wetting" action of water constituting a part of the cosmetic formula, and the "humectant" action of a hygroscopic ingredient (such as glycerol, sorbitol or other suitable polyol).

Correct proportioning of these ingredients is essential in order to prevent some undesirable effects, *e.g.*, tissue dehydration owing to excessive hygroscopic action by the wrong kind or wrong proportion of the humectant employed.

It is noteworthy, in this connection, that in experiments upon sections of corneous tissue (callus) prolonged contact with lipoid materials (oils, fats, lanolin, etc.) did not restore pliability to the brittle horny material, whereas immersion in water or maintenance in a humid atmosphere did. This is the reason why modern cosmetic formulation stresses the so-called "moisturizing" action of conditioning (and other) cosmetics, and why a number of older, "greasy" cosmetics have been reformulated so as to yield "greaseless" products, i.e., those with a comparatively low content of lipoid matter, but exhibiting the capacity of increasing the water content of the *stratum corneum*. A relatively occlusive lipoid film on the skin surface will be additionally helpful in reducing the moisture loss from the skin.

It may be mentioned in passing that there is reason to postulate the existence of a "natural moisturizing factor." Its presence may be established by extracting cornified epithelium first with an organic solvent (to remove the lipids), followed by water which removes a significant amount of a hygroscopic material. The latter has been assumed to represent the water holding principle of the *stratum corneum*. It consists, to the extent of some 40 per cent, of free amino acids of which 16 have been identified; however, the entire active portion of this substance remains unknown. Some cosmetic creams contain a protein hydrolysate as an ingredient which is intended to impart to the skin a comparable water-binding capacity.

There exists some evidence as to differences in the adsorption tendency of the skin for the different "fats," depending upon their chemical character and composition. Thus lanolin, also certain fatty oils (of both vegetable and animal origin) appear to be adsorbed more readily than, e.g., petrolatum; incidentally, such adsorption (or absorption) may reach into the gland ducts where it takes place along their epithelial lining.

Actually the number of natural and hydrogenated fats, oils and waxes employed as components of conditioning creams and lotions is very large, and special advantages are being attributed to each of them, sometimes on rational, but often on putative grounds. Moreover, in the more recent past new materials of synthetic origin have entered the picture in great numbers. For illustrative purposes, it is deemed desirable to review briefly some of the more important initial materials, before discussing the cosmetic formulations in which they are employed.

Hydrocarbons

From the large class of hydrocarbons, mineral oil, petrolatum, paraffin, ceresin and ozokerite are used quite extensively. All of them consist substantially of mixed saturated aliphatic or cyclic hydrocarbons. It will be remembered that a hydrocarbon can occur in a gaseous, liquid, semi-solid or solid state, depending upon the size of the molecule of the particular aliphatic or alicyclic compound; thus methane, CH_4, the simplest hydrocarbon, is a gas; octane, C_8H_{18}, is a liquid, while triacontane, $C_{30}H_{62}$, is a solid. Petrolatum is a mixture of semi-solid hydrocarbons obtained from petroleum, while mineral oil (also known as liquid paraffin or liquid petrolatum) is a mixture of liquid hydrocarbons from the same source. Paraffin, ozokerite and ceresin are different types of mixtures of solid hydrocarbons; the designation "mineral wax" or "earth wax," as applied alternately to the latter two materials, could mislead in that neither is a true wax (i.e., a *monoester* of a particular composition as to the participating fatty acids and alcohols).

Fats and Oils

The fats and oils of vegetable and animal origin belong to the class of triglycerides, i.e., fatty acid tri-esters of glycerol. The component fatty acid (acyl) radicals can be saturated or unsaturated. Their chain lengths, degrees of unsaturation and relative positions in the molecule determine the character of the fat or fatty oil. Thus a triglyceride of the (saturated) palmitic or stearic acids (i.e., solid fatty acids with sixteen and eighteen carbon atoms respectively) will be a solid. Oleic acid is liquid at room temperature; it is an unsaturated fatty acid with eighteen carbon atoms and one double bond. It occurs in olive oil, also in peanut and sesame oils. Linseed oil contains linoleic and linolenic acids (in addition to oleic, palmitic and stearic acids). These acids are still more unsaturated in character; there are two double bonds in the molecule of linoleic acid, and three in that of linolenic acid.

The relationship of the several C_{18}-acids (i.e., fatty acids with eighteen carbon atoms) mentioned is illustrated by the following group of formulas:

$$CH_3(CH_2)_4CH_2CH_2CH_2CH_2CH_2CH_2CH_2CH_2CH_2(CH_2)_3COOH$$

Stearic Acid

$$CH_3(CH_2)_4CH_2CH_2CH_2CH{=}CHCH_2CH_2CH_2CH_2(CH_2)_3COOH$$

Oleic Acid

$$CH_3(CH_2)_4CH{=}CHCH_2CH{=}CHCH_2CH_2CH_2CH_2(CH_2)_3COOH$$

Linoleic Acid

$$CH_3(CH_2)_4CH{=}CHCH_2CH{=}CHCH_2CH{=}CHCH_2(CH_2)_3COOH$$

Linolenic Acid

Vegetable oils make satisfactory ingredients of cosmetic preparations by contributing both emollient and occlusive properties, but their unsaturated character introduces the problem of adequacy of shelf life because of their proneness to oxidation and rancidity. While hydrogenation would eliminate unsaturation, it would affect, at the same time, the character of the material, e.g., changing a liquid oil into a solid fat; such a change might then render a given material less desirable for use. Therefore, where the formula calls for a vegetable oil, one employs a judiciously selected anti-oxidant chemical which should combine satisfactory protective action for the oil with freedom from any untoward (i.e., irritant or sensitizing) effect upon the skin. Although an anti-oxidant substance is added, as a rule, in minute proportions, its presence in a particular cosmetic may be of dermatological significance, because it, rather than any major component of the formula, may be involved in a dermal reaction; yet, because of the minuteness of its proportion, an independent chemical analysis may not always disclose its presence, thereby vitiating any attempt to identify a possibly offending agent.

In the recent past, a considerable number of synthetic materials have come into use as ingredients of cosmetic products, as substitutes for, or supplements to, the natural fats, oils and waxes. Some of them correspond to the natural triglycerides in that they, too, are based upon glycerol; beyond this, however, many of these synthetics are derived from mono- and polyhydric alcohols in general.

Thus butyl stearate, a useful cosmetic ingredient of the formula $C_{17}H_{35}.COOC_4H_9$, is an oleagenous material obtained by esterification of stearic acid with butyl alcohol. Another widely used oil is isopropyl myristate with the formula $C_{15}H_{31}COOCH(CH_3)_2$.

In the case of a polyhydric alcohol, the esterification may be either total or partial; if it is partial, i.e., if one or more hydroxyl groups are left free from engagement with fatty acids, the compounds exhibit a measure of hydrophilic quality which depends, among other things, upon the number of free hydroxyl groups present. The simplest illustration is furnished by ethylene glycol:

$$\begin{array}{c} CH_2OH \\ \cdot \\ CH_2OH \end{array}$$

which can be esterified either in one or both positions. In the case of glycerol, esterification may occur in one, two or three positions. As a matter of fact, the technical grade of glyceryl monostearate is known to contain varying proportions of the di- and tristearates.

Waxes

Chemically speaking, the designation "wax" applies to the esters of high-molecular fatty acids with high-molecular monohydric alcohols; however, the term "wax" is being applied occasionally to a variety of substances which resemble the true waxes in their physical appearance although they bear no chemical relation to them.

Most true waxes are either of animal or of vegetable origin. Among the most important are beeswax, spermaceti, carnauba and candelilla wax.

The chief constituent of beeswax (about 80 per cent) is myricyl palmitate of the formula $C_{15}H_{31}COOCH_{30}H_{61}$.

Important is its content of free fatty acids, *viz.*, cerotic and melissic, the former a saturated hexacosanoic acid ($C_{25}H_{51}COOH$), the latter a saturated triacontanoic acid ($C_{29}H_{59}COOH$); as will be remembered, these free acids are involved in the formation of the beeswax-borax emulsions, as, e.g., in the preparation of cold cream.

The main constituent of spermaceti is cetyl palmitate:

$$C_{15}H_{31}COOC_{16}H_{31}$$

Present are also cetyl esters of lauric, myristic and stearic acid, as well as free cetyl alcohol (1-hexadecanol):

$$C_{16}H_{33}OH.$$

"Carbowaxes"

Reference was made before to the so-called "mineral waxes" which are in reality solid hydrocarbons rather than true waxes (monoesters). Of an entirely different character are the "Carbowaxes" which also are not monoesters, but rather polyethylene and methoxypolyethylene glycols, with molecular weights ranging from 200 to 7500. Unlike either the true waxes or the mineral waxes, the "Carbowaxes" are soluble in water, which renders them suitable in the preparation of "washable" creams and ointments. Mixtures of different solid polymers may be prepared with liquid polyethylene glycols, leading to products of ointment consistency. The basic formula of a polyethylene glycol is:

$$HO.CH_2CH_2(CH_2OCH_2)_nCH_2OH.$$

Their mono-fatty acid esters are non-ionic surfactants.

Lanolin and Derived Materials

Lanolin takes a somewhat special position in the group of initial materials for cosmetics. Its greatest proportion is composed of fatty acid esters of high molecular weight alcohols, such as cholesterol, also lanosterol, agnosterol and others. This would make lanolin appear to answer the description of a "wax"; accordingly, the customary reference to lanolin as "wool-fat" would appear to be a misnomer since there are no triglycerides in lanolin. Although the opinion is prevalent that lanolin, among the different cosmetic materials, is the one material most closely resembling human sebum "the natural skin lubricant," there is a distinct difference between the composition of the latter and that of sheep sebum, the raw material of lanolin.

With the aid of modern refining methods, lanolin can be rendered light in color and free from odor. It is mostly in this form that it is used extensively in cosmetics. It represents a rather complex mixture of mono-, di- and polyesters of hydroxy-aliphatic and other acids with sterols, and with triterpenoid as well as high-molecular aliphatic mono- and dihydric alcohols. The wax ester content is about 96 per cent. When saponified, lanolin yields about 25 per cent of cholesterol and the same proportion of triterpenoid alcohols (mostly lano- and dihydrolanosterol); according to more recent findings, the latter alcohols exhibit a ring structure similar to that of the sterols.

Lanolin is credited with being an effective skin emollient. By modern definition, an emollient is an agent capable of softening dry horny tissue by inducing its rehydration; the latter effect is due to a lowering of the evaporation rate of insensible perspiration owing to the formation of an occlusive film over the skin surface. Contrary to older opinion, more recent findings indicate that lanolin does not penetrate the skin; actually, this should be somewhat of an advantage, since penetration would signify a change in the normal condition of the epidermis. By not penetrating, a lanolin film helps maintain the epidermis in a normal state.

Lanolin's capacity to absorb and to hold water is somewhat obscure as to its origin; it may be due to the presence of secondary alcohols.

In the recent past a great number of products have been placed on the market which utilize lanolin as their source.

Thus, by a process of fractionated chilling, lanolin is made to yield a liquid portion in the form of a heavy oil which, unlike lanolin itself, shows good solubility in mineral oil; this is why it is used, among other things, in the formulation of "baby oils."

Saponification of lanolin and fractional vacuum distillation of its unsaponifiable portion yields a number of mixed "lanolin alcohols." Certain fractions which are soluble in ethanol are used, e.g., in pressure packaged hair lacquers to serve as hair fixatives, also as plasticizers for other more brittle film-forming components.

An important isolate of lanolin is cholesterol which is employed as initial material for a variety of derivatives.

It is noteworthy that certain fractions of lanolin alcohols serve as functional components of the so-called *"absorption bases."* These are essentially mixtures of mineral type hydrocarbons with lanolin alcohols, sometimes with auxiliary emulsifying agents added. The absorption bases exhibit an enhanced capacity for forming water-in-oil emulsions. This makes them valuable in the formulation of emollients, ointments, etc., or as additives to creams, lotions, and other cosmetics with emollient properties. Absorption bases are also employed as "super-fatting" agents for soaps.

Since lanolin contains a number of components with free hydroxyl groups, esterification with acetic or propionic anhydride produces modifications with new properties. Unlike the original product, acetylated lanolin is entirely hydrophobic, i.e., devoid of any capacity to form water-in-oil emulsions; it is also soluble in cold mineral oil. Acetylation of isolated lanolin alcohols also leads to a hydrophobic (lipophilic) product, soluble not only in mineral and vegetable oils (including castor oil), but also in ethanol and in ethyl acetate. Other esters are those of mixed lanolin alcohols with castor oil fatty acids or with polyunsaturated fatty acids; they represent true wax esters. All of these esters find extensive use in all types of cosmetics, also in many pharmaceutical specialties.

Another group of lanolin derivatives is obtained by condensation with ethylene oxide. Polyoxyethylene chains form ether linkages to the hydroxyesters present in lanolin, thereby enhancing the hydrophilic character gradually until a point of "solubility" in water is reached; actually, the product is not soluble, but it forms a transparent colloidal dispersion. Polyoxyethylene lanolin derivatives of varying ethylene oxide polymer chain lengths are used in a wide variety of cosmetics including hair dressings, deodorant sticks, cold waves and many others.

Ethylene oxide derivatives of lanolin alcohols and hydroxyesters can also be acetylated to yield solubilizing (dispersing) agents for different water insoluble materials, including mineral oil and essential oils.

The p-aminobenzoic esters of certain lanolin alcohols combine the sun screening action of p-aminobenzoic acid with the emollient effect of lanolin.

The above limited selection of examples represents but a small fraction of the tremendous number of new products derived from lanolin which only a short while ago constituted a single, rather well defined entity in the armamentarium of initial materials.

Having reviewed a number of important materials entering into the composition of *conditioning creams,* consideration may now be given to some illustrative formulas.

A simple mixture possessed of emollient qualities might consist of the following ingredients:

Conditioning Cream

	Per Cent
Lanolin, anhydrous	70.0
Petrolatum	18.0
Sweet almond oil	12.0

The formula depends for its emollient action primarily upon its lanolin content. The purpose of adding petrolatum and sweet almond oil is to thin out the mixture, making its application easier, and reducing the "tackiness" of the lanolin which, by itself, would be too viscid to spread readily on the skin.

Two emulsified conditioning creams of simple composition are illustrated below:

Emulsified Conditioning Creams

	Per Cent	
Lanolin	50.0	25.0
Lanolin alcohols	15.0	15.0
Mineral oil	—	25.0
Water	35.0	35.0

Gradual addition of water with stirring to the uniform melt of the fatty components will cause a water-in-oil type of emulsion to form. The end product will have the consistency of an ointment.

The "Hydrophilic Ointment" of the U.S. Pharmacopeia which is free from lanolin, contains sodium lauryl sulfate as an emulsifying agent. The formula of this simple water-in-oil emulsion type of ointment follows:

Hydrophilic Ointment (U.S.P.)

	Per Cent
Stearyl alcohol	25.0
Petrolatum, white	25.0
Propylene glycol	12.0
Sodium lauryl sulfate	1.0
Water	37.0
Preservative	q.s.

(The preservative consists here of 0.025% methylparaben and 0.015% propylparaben.)

As indicated elsewhere, in the more recent past the "humectant" aspect of emolliency has been growing in importance, as against the "lubricating" effect of the film-forming fatty components of conditioning creams. This is why recent publicity is replete with references to the "moisturizing" action of different cosmetics. On this premise, some of the newer, more modern conditioning creams and lotions contain a lower proportion of fatty emollients, and a comparatively higher one of water and polyhydric alcohols (polyols). They exhibit the humectant quality in that they reduce the evaporation rate of water. Some of these polyols are propylene glycol, glycerol and sorbitol.

A "moisturizing" cream formula of this type might be composed as follows:

Moisturizing Cream

	Per Cent
Stearic acid	15.0
Lanolin	5.0
Beeswax	2.0
Mineral oil	20.0
d-Sorbitol (70%)	13.0
Sorbitan trioleate (Arlacel 85)	1.0
Polyoxyethylene sorbitan trioleate (Tween 85)	1.0
Water	43.0

Incidentally, sorbitol which is listed in the above formula is a hexahydric alcohol obtained by hydrogenation of natural sugars. While it retards the loss of moisture, it does not produce a damp sensation on the skin, as may be caused by a more hygroscopic polyol.

It should be added for the sake of completeness that there are published data connecting lanolin with eczematous hypersensitivity. This effect has been attributed to some hydroxyl-bearing components of lanolin, probably certain hydroxy-fatty acids. Actually, esterification with propionic, also with acetic acid was found to produce better tolerance in those cases which reacted adversely to untreated lanolin. With this as a premise, an emollient ointment can be formulated which does not contain any lanolin as such, but features two lanolin products that are free from suspicion of exerting a sensitizing potential. The following formula is of the water-in-oil emulsion type:

Conditioning Cream

	Per Cent
Acetylated lanolin (Modulan)	10.0
Lanolin alcohol base (Amerchol L101)	10.0
Petrolatum, liquid	20.0
Microcrystalline wax (170 W-Bareco)	10.0
Sorbitan sesquioleate (Arlacel 83)	2.0
Sorbitol (Sorbo)	3.0
Water	45.0

As in the case of certain other cosmetics preparations, so also in the case of conditioning creams a distinction should be made with regard to the type of skin for which a particular formula is recommended. Thus, a rich cream, i.e., one full of fatty matter should not be suggested for use on an oily skin, nor one consisting substantially of mineral oil for an asteatotic skin (owing to the effective solvent action of mineral oil upon sebum, resulting in a "drying" effect upon the skin).

PRESERVATION OF COSMETICS

Reference was made elsewhere to the use of a "preservative." Since most cosmetic preparations call for preservation, it is deemed logical to review this subject at an early stage, particularly in view of its dermatological interest.

Two types of chemicals are employed to prolong the shelf-life of a cosmetic product, as well as its stability while in use by the consumer, *viz., preservatives* and *antioxidants*. The former are generally understood to be substances capable of preventing spoilage due to microbial action, while the latter are employed to retard oxidative deterioration, particularly that of fats and oils. Some chemicals exhibit both properties.

While it is an *a priori* requirement that preservatives and antioxidants should be non-toxic, non-irritant and non-sensitizing, it is well to keep this class of chemicals in mind in connection with any so-called cosmetic skin reactions which may be called to the dermatologist's attention.

Preservatives

Both fungi and bacteria, usually of air-borne origin, can cause contamination, followed by partial or total deterioration of the cosmetic product. Many ingredients of cosmetic creams and lotions can serve as substrates for microbial growth and multiplication. Among them are carbohydrates (such as natural gums, starches and sugars), fats (including vegetable oils and waxes) and proteins (as well as peptones and aminoacids), also polyhydric alcohols (e.g., glycerol, sorbitol).

Among the more common preservatives are the following:

Organic Acids. Benzoic, monochloroacetic, propionic and sorbic acids act as antimicrobial agents usually in undissociated form, rather than as salts or ions; their effectiveness depends therefore upon the pH of the medium.

Alcohols. Ethyl and isopropyl alcohols are effective as preservatives when present in concentrations of 10 to 15 per cent, except that at pH above 7 higher concentrations may be required. Although chlorobutanol (1,1,1-trichloro-2-methyl-2-propanol) is being used to preserve a number of liquid pharmaceuticals and biologicals, its pungent odor militates against any routine application in preserving cosmetics.

Aldehydes. Formaldehyde is used occasionally where its reactivity (e.g., with the aminogroups of proteins) is not a bar. While benzaldehyde is without appreciable preserving efficacy, cinnamic aldehyde, with its broad spectrum of antimicrobial action, may be employed where its characteristic odor is not objectionable.

Essential Oils. The subject of essential oils will be reviewed in some detail in connection with the discussion of perfumes. Suffice it to say at this point that some of these natural distillates contain active antimicrobial constituents (e.g., thymol, in oil of thyme) which are capable of exerting preservative action.

Quaternary Ammonium Compounds. Numerous compounds

belonging in this category exhibit inhibitory action upon bacteria. Their antimicrobial effectiveness is greater in alkaline than in acid media. However, their incompatibility characteristics (e.g., with respect to emulsifying agents of the anionic class) tend to limit their usefulness as preservatives.

Mercurials. The toxicity of organic mercurials demands caution, and therefore stands in the way of any extensive use in the preservation of cosmetics; however, several phenylmercuric salts (borate, benzoate, salicylate) are employed occasionally, e.g., in waving lotions, bentonite gels, and in other special instances. Inorganic mercury salts are too corrosive as well as too toxic for any routine use.

Dehydroacetic Acid. Because of its claimed non-irritant and non-sensitizing character, this chemical is used occasionally in cosmetics to inhibit bacterial or fungal proliferation.

Phenol Derivatives. Among the more important phenol derivatives employed as preservatives are o-phenylphenol, p-chloro-m-cresol, p-chloro-m-xylenol, chlorothymol, also hexachlorophene and bithionol. The latter two chemicals have been mentioned before in connection with deodorant soaps, and will be referred to again in the formulation of cosmetic deodorants.

Esters of p-Hydroxybenzoic Acid. The compounds of this class may be considered as phenol derivatives. The different members (methyl, ethyl, propyl, butyl and benzyl esters) are being used quite extensively as preservatives because of their marked bacteriostatic and fungistatic efficiency, coupled with virtual freedom from toxicity and irritancy. Incidentally, the p-hydroxybenzoates exhibit also a measure of antioxidant action.

Antioxidants

When spontaneous oxidation of the unsaturated components of fats or oils has progressed to the point of organoleptic detection of such oxidation products, "rancidity" is in evidence. It is characterized by the presence of certain oxidative degradation products, such as aldehydes, ketones and short-chain fatty acids which contribute to the typical "rancid" odor. To retard or prevent this process of deterioration, antioxidant chemicals are employed whose function is to prevent the uptake of oxygen by the susceptible material.

It is noteworthy that natural antioxidants are associated with different vegetable oils in their original state; they consist mostly of tocopherols. They are found in the unsaponifiable fraction, but are removed almost entirely by the refining process.

Moisture, light, heat, also the activity of certain microorganisms may accelerate the development of rancidity. Contact with certain metals may have a "pro-oxidant" effect, copper being one of the worst offenders in this respect.

The cosmetic chemist has a number of different classes of antioxidant chemicals at his disposal, as shown by the following selective listing:

Phenolic Type. Gallic acid (3,4,5-trihydroxybenzoic acid) and its esters (amyl and propyl gallate), p-hydroxybenzoic esters (methyl through butyl p-hydroxybenzoates), 2,5-di-*tert*butyl-p-cresol, hydroquinone and its alkyl derivatives (e.g., 2,5-di-*tert*-butyl hydroquinone), guaiacol (also gum guaiac) and others.

Quinone Type. Tocopherols, hydroxycoumarans, hydroxychromans.

Amine Type. Lecithin, ethanolamine, glutamic acid, purines.

Organic Acids, Alcohols, and Esters. Ascorbic, malonic, citric and thiopropionic acids; mannitol and sorbitol; isopropyl citrate and dilauryl thiopropionate.

Inorganic. Phosphoric and phosphorous acids, and their salts.

Antioxidants act to prevent the oxygen take-up by susceptible materials, or to undergo oxidation themselves. It is conceivable that some of the more reactive among them may enter into a combination with some tissue proteins, thus giving rise to the formation of potentially allergenic matter. This is why it may be important, in diagnosing a case of cosmetic dermatitis, to inquire into the possibility of an antioxidant or a preservative serving, e.g., as a sensitizing agent.

Chapter 5

FOUNDATION COSMETICS

THE PREPARATIONS belonging in this category usually have a double function; they serve as foundations for make-up (powder, rouge), but they may also be capable of guarding the skin against the damaging action of environmental factors, such as heat and cold, wind and weather.

One of the oldest types of foundations is the "vanishing cream"; essentially, this is a dispersion of stearic acid (or of some other crystalline fatty acid) in a stearate or other suitable fatty acid salt (of sodium, potassium, ammonium or of certain aliphatic amino compounds).

Thus, when stearic acid is made to react with an alkali hydroxide or carbonate, or with ammonia or an aliphatic amine (the proportions being such that the acid is stoichiometrically in excess for complete neutralization), the stearate forming in the course of the reaction acts as an emulsifying agent for the unreacted acid. Such creams develop a characteristic "pearliness" on standing owing to the gradual crystallization of the free stearic acid in a finely dispersed state.

Since in the preparation of this type of vanishing cream a salt of a long-chain fatty acid is formed, one meets occasionally with the statement that because of the presumed soap-like character of this compound, a vanishing cream must exhibit an alkaline reaction. Actually, this is not the case, as the pH of vanishing creams is usually below 7. This is probably due to the formation of "acid salts," as represented, e.g., by the molecular compound of potassium stearate with stearic acid in definite proportions.

However, vanishing creams may be prepared also without the participation of fatty acid salts as dispersing agents. In this case advantage is taken of some suitable non-ionic emulsifier or a combination of such emulsifiers.

Desirable humectancy is imparted to a vanishing cream by means of a polyol. This helps protect the cream from drying out, and it also causes the application of make-up to adhere to the skin better and longer; moreover, a measure of protective action is afforded the skin against weathering. Glycerol, propylene glycol, sorbitol are some of the polyols suitable for incorporation in vanishing creams. Added emolliency may be obtained with the aid of moderate proportions of ingredients such as lanolin or some of its derivatives, cetyl alcohol, etc.

Below is an illustrative formula for a vanishing cream which utilizes ammonium stearate as its emulsifying (dispersing) principle:

Vanishing Cream

	Per Cent
Stearic acid	25.0
Glycerol	10.0
Ammonia (26%)	1.5
Water	63.5
Preservative	q.s.

A vanishing cream free from any "soap-like" components is illustrated by the following formulas:

Vanishing Cream

	Per Cent
Stearic acid	15.0
Sorbitol	7.5
Sorbitan monostearate (Arlacel 60)	2.0
Polyoxyethylene sorbitan monostearate (Tween 60)	1.5
Water	74.0
Preservative	q.s.

Although the discussion of make-up (face powder, rouge, etc.) is reserved for another chapter, it may be mentioned here that certain modern foundation creams are formulated so as to yield a make-up effect upon application to the skin. This calls for the incorporation of opacifying agents and inorganic pigments, preferably in a "greaseless" vanishing cream base (although fatty cream bases are also used for this purpose). Following is an example of an emollient, tinted foundation cream which can be used without or with make-up, and which employs a combination of triethanolammonium and sodium stearates as the dispersing principle:

Foundation Cream (tinted)

	Per Cent
Stearic acid	10.0
Mineral oil	15.0
Lanolin	7.0
Cetyl alcohol	2.0
Triethanolamine	1.5
Borax	0.5
Propylene glycol	5.0
Pigments	3.0
Water	56.0
Preservative	q.s.

The "pigments" mentioned in this formula usually include zinc oxide or titanium dioxide, plus insoluble mineral colors (iron oxides) such as ochre, sienna, etc.; they are blended in different proportions, thus producing the various "shades" of the finished product to match the skin of the individual user.

In the same category belong the special "blemish covers" which are more highly pigmented preparations intended to conceal skin blemishes such as birth marks, chloasma, vitiliginous areas, and the like. They may be made in the form of creams (ointments), or in solidified form as "sticks"; the principle involved in producing the latter form will be discussed in connection with the formulation of lipsticks.

HAND CREAMS AND LOTIONS

The primary purpose of a hand cream or lotion is to keep the skin of the hands soft and pliable, by counteracting the deleterious effects of exposure, especially to soap and other detergents which tend to emulsify and remove much of the protective sebum, thereby causing the skin to become dry, scaly or even fissured. The beneficial action of a well formulated hand cream should extend also to protection against atmospheric conditions (heat, cold and wind) which may affect the skin unfavorably by causing roughness, chapping and cracking.

Since the composition of hand creams usually resembles that of vanishing creams, it is deemed logical to discuss them in this context.

A simple hand cream employing potassium stearate (produced *in situ*) as its emulsifying agent may be prepared according to the following formula:

Hand Cream

	Per Cent
Stearic acid	15.0
Stearyl alcohol	2.0
Propylene glycol monostearate	1.0
Glycerol	7.0
Potassium carbonate	1.0
Water	74.0
Preservative	q.s.

Below is another hand cream formula, free of the "soap-like" potassium stearate; here emulsification is effected with the aid of a combination of certain non-ionic surfactants:

Hand Cream

	Per Cent
Stearic acid	10.0
Sorbitol	5.0
Sorbitan monostearate (Arlacel 60)	5.0
Sorbitan monoleate (Arlacel 80)	1.0
Polyoxyethylene sorbitan monostearate (Tween 60)	3.0
Water	76.0
Preservative	q.s.

For the sake of greater emollient effectiveness, ingredients of lipid character (e.g., lanolin) can be incorporated in different hand cream formulas in discreet proportions, i.e., without rendering the finished product unsatisfactory in use because of a "greasy" or "sticky" sensation.

Popular also are *hand lotions.* A preparation representing an oil-in-water type of system might be produced from the following formula:

Hand Lotion

	Per Cent
Stearic acid	5.0
Cetyl alcohol	0.5
Glycerol	3.0
Triethanolamine	0.5
Sodium alginate	0.5
Alcohol	5.0
Water	85.5
Preservative	q.s.

To prepare such an emulsion, the melt of the "fatty" components, i.e., stearic acid and cetyl alcohol, heated to 70°C is added under rapid stirring to the aqueous solution of triethanolamine, glycerol, sodium alginate and preservative (e.g. methyl hydroxybenzoate) also heated to 70°C. Stirring is continued. When the temperature has dropped to 40°C, alcohol is added (in which some perfume may have been dissolved), and stirring is stopped at 30°C. In the course of this process, triethanolammonium stearate is formed *in situ* which acts as the emulsifying principle. Sodium alginate is a thickening agent which acts to change a "milky" consistency to a "creamy" one.

Other thickening agents may be selected from the class of vegetable gums and mucilages (e.g., gum karaya, quince seed), or from the class of synthetic or semi-synthetic thickeners (e.g., methyl cellulose).

As in the case of the "solid" creams, so also in that of the lotions, emulsification can be effected with the aid of non-ionic surfactants. An illustrative formula follows:

Hand Lotion

	Per Cent
Stearic acid	5.0
Lanolin	1.0
Sorbitan monoleate (Arlacel 80)	0.5
Polyoxyethylene sorbitan monostearate (Tween 60)	2.5
Sorbitol	3.5
Water	87.5
Preservative	q.s.

In the more recent past, certain types of silicones have come into use as ingredients of protective hand cosmetics. They are credited with an occlusive effectiveness capable of warding off any undesirable action upon the skin of soaps and detergents, and, incidentally, of a variety of contact allergens. (They are less effective, as a rule, against organic solvents, industrial oils, and the like). An example of a suitable type of silicone oil is a dimethylpolysiloxane polymer (of 250-500 centistokes viscosity) of the following schematic formula:

```
      CH3      CH3      CH3
      |        |        |
  -O- Si  -O-  Si  -O-  Si -
      |        |        |
      CH3      CH2      CH3
```

Some hand creams and lotions contain allantoin, the diureide of glyoxylic acid, with the formula on next page.

Allantoin is claimed to promote granulation, thereby accelerat-

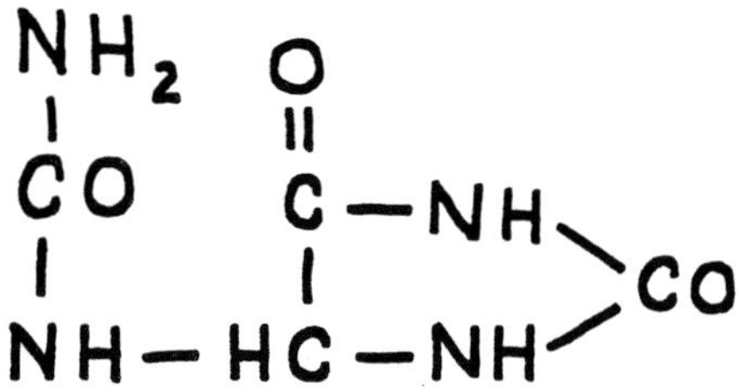

```
NH2   O
|     ||
CO    C—NH
|     |     \
|     |      CO
|     |     /
NH—HC—NH
```

ing the healing process of a skin cracked or chapped by exposure ("dishpan hands").

It may be of some historic interest that the "glycerin-rose water lotion" probably represents one of the oldest preparations for the care of the hands. Originally this product was composed of equal parts of rose water and glycerol, but subsequently the proportion of glycerol was reduced to 25 per cent or less. A variation of the "glycerin-rose water lotion" contains added gum tragacanth or irish moss, serving not only to increase the viscosity of the mixture, but also to produce a smooth sensation on the hands, probably brought about by the gum "sealing" the crevices of an originally rough or chapped skin.

For the sake of completeness, brief reference may be made at this point to "*all-purpose*" creams. As this name implies, such creams are intended to combine the respective functions of the several cream types designed for special purposes, and more particularly those of the cleansing, conditioning and foundation creams. Obviously, it is not to be expected that an "all-purpose" cream will render an optimal performance for a particular purpose, as compared with a special preparation compounded for such a purpose. Nor is it feasible to apply here the desirable principle of a specialized composition with respect to a particular skin type demanding it. Nevertheless, these creams enjoy a measure of public acceptance, especially where economy is a prime consideration.

Chapter 6

MAKE-UP

THE BASIC ITEMS of make-up are face powder, lipsticks and rouges.

FACE POWDER

The essential purpose of a face powder is to create a mat, velvety finish on the skin by covering the "greasy" shine produced particularly by sebaceous secretion. Another important purpose is to minimize the appearance of minor imperfections of the skin. Both effects are achieved primarily by means of an opaque white pigment, such as zinc oxide or titanium dioxide; however, this must be combined with other materials in order to avoid unnatural looking whiteness or opacity.

A face powder may contain few or many ingredients. However, most face powders contain in addition to one of the oxides mentioned, the following components with specialized functions: talc, kaolin, zinc (or magnesium) stearate, coloring matter, and perfume.

Talc is a hydrated magnesium silicate of mineral origin. Its formula is $3\ MgO.4SiO_2.H_2O$. It has two functions to perform, *viz.*, to serve as a diluent for the white opaque pigment, and to impart to the powder the quality of "slip," i.e., the capacity for smooth and easy spreading on the skin. Most powders contain at least 50 per cent of talc.

Kaolin is a natural aluminum silicate with the formula $2SiO_2.Al_2O_3.2H_2O$. Its primary purpose is to act as an absorbent for perspiration. Since it has no "slip," it is always combined with talc;

incidentally, the undesirable "shine" of talc is minimized or eliminated by the presence of kaolin.

Zinc and magnesium stearates are characterized by an extremely low "packing density," thus contributing the quality of "fluffiness" to the face powder; they also enhance the adherence of the powder to the skin. Occasionally, one encounters stearates of other metals (e.g., of aluminum or calcium), also of other fatty acids (e.g., undecylenic) as ingredients of face powders.

It should be mentioned in passing that purified grades of calcium and magnesium carbonates are also found in a number of face powders.

All face powders are produced in a wide variety of shades in order to blend with individual skin colorings. Nowadays, only insoluble inorganic and organic pigments are used for this purpose. The former are drawn mostly from the list of pure iron oxides and hydroxides, and include the synthetic ochres, umbers and siennas; the latter are lake colors obtained by precipitation of originally soluble coal-tar dyes, with or upon certain inorganic compounds such as calcium chloride, aluminum hydroxide etc., and subsequent processing which leads eventually to a powdered material of impalpable fineness.

Finally, all face powders contain perfume (in common with most other cosmetic products). However, with respect to face powders, it might be of possible dermatological significance that unlike in the case of creams or lotions, the perfume here is not diluted with a solvent; instead, infinitesimally small particles of the concentrate are distributed throughout the powder, a factor which might conceivably play a role in a cutaneous reaction claimed to be due to the use of some particular face powder. This matter will be considered more fully under another heading, *viz.*, that of "Perfumes."

For the sake of completeness it should be added here that face powders may contain occasionally ingredients other than those listed above, such as rice starch, "powdered silk," etc. As to the former, its use abroad is more popular than in this country, where it has been criticized (on putative rather than on factual grounds) for its tendency to cake in the presence of moisture, also for its availability as a nutrient for microorganisms.

The term "powdered silk" is a misnomer since one of the steps in the production of this material calls for the treatment of the silk fiber with a strong acid or alkali which, of course, will bring about at least a partial hydrolysis of the silk protein (i.e., to the peptone stage). After drying, the hydrolysate is ground to an impalpable powder.

There is no reason to believe that "powdered silk" offers any cosmetic or therapeutic advantage. It is employed most likely for psychological and promotional reasons because of the obvious suggestiveness of the term "silk" with reference to a widely used cosmetic such as face powder.

Depending upon their opacity, face powders are produced in several "weights." A sample formula of a "medium weight" face powder follows:

Face Powder

	Per Cent
Talc	50.0
Kaolin	15.0
Zinc oxide	15.0
Calcium carbonate	10.0
Magnesium carbonate	5.0
Zinc stearate	5.0
Pigments	q.s.
Perfume	q.s.

Compact powders (or powder compacts) are obtained by compressing mixtures similar to the above in the presence of a suitable "binder" such as gum tragacanth, gum arabic, quince seed mucilage and the like. Some powder compacts employ either a soap-like substance (such as sodium stearate) or a non-ionic surfactant as a binder. A similar binder principle is employed in producing "cake make-up" which calls for the use of a moist sponge or a moist piece of cotton in order to pick up the required amount of "make-up" and to spread it on the face.

A rouge compact (compact rouge) generally corresponds in composition to the powder compact, except that the particular type of coloring matter is selected to fit its intended purpose; moreover, the proportion of pigment is higher here than in the case of powder compacts.

Powders and rouges are also produced with ointment or cream bases; they, too, employ (insoluble) pigments and color lakes as a rule. The vogue for liquid rouges containing soluble colors dissolved in water and suitably thickened (e.g., with the aid of methyl cellulose, sodium alginate, etc.) is receding owing to the greater difficulty in correcting a faulty application to the skin.

LIPSTICKS

While the practice of coloring lips has been going on since the dawn of antiquity, the lipstick is of comparatively recent origin. Its technical development and popular acceptance coincide with the introduction of suitable synthetic colors, particularly those capable of producing an "indelible" stain upon the lips.

In the modern lipstick, the coloring matter is dispersed in, and carried by, the lipstick "base." The latter consists of a blend of certain oils and waxes among which castor oil plays a prominent role because of its capacity to act as a solvent for a group of dyes (notably certain fluorescein derivatives), employed to stain the lips. Actually, it could be said that the lipstick base is "built" around its castor oil component, the other ingredients of the base serving to "solidify" the (liquid) castor oil, and to impart to the base certain desirable characteristics, especially in regard to the ease of application of the finished article.

The following formula will illustrate the composition of a simple but acceptable lipstick base:

Lipstick Base

	Per Cent
Castor oil	65.0
Beeswax	15.0
Carnauba wax	10.0
Lanolin	10.0
Preservative	q.s.

Here the combination of carnauba wax and beeswax contributes the solidifying principle which renders the mixture suitable for forming into sticks when poured into a chilled mold and allowed to set. (Lanolin is added for its emollient effect, also to help make the lipstick "come off" in the proper amount upon application to the lips.)

Other materials are employed additionally in compounding the lipstick base. Among them may be certain hydrogenated fats and oils, cocoa butter, petrolatum, mineral waxes, cetyl alcohol, etc. They are added for the sake of achieving some special desirable characteristics, such as high gloss, good adhesion and freedom from tackiness.

The lipstick "base" is combined with special coloring matter to yield the lipstick "mass." This coloring matter occurs in two co-existent forms, *viz.*, as "active" dyes and "inert" color lakes. The dyes stain the skin, in the true sense of this word, thereby supplying the "indelible" principle. By contrast, the color lakes are insoluble, non-reactive pigments, i.e., without any staining action upon the lip tissue. (They are obtained by precipitation of dyes with the aid of certain salts which, in the case of the cosmetic lakes, are usually those of aluminum or of the alkaline earths, such as calcium or strontium.)

To produce the lipstick mass, one would combine the above lipstick base (or some part of it, preferably its oil component) with a mixture consisting of the following: dyes (halogenated fluoresceins) 2 to 5 per cent and color lakes 10 to 15 per cent, based upon the total lipstick base. For the sake of obtaining a uniform distribution of the color particles, the mechanism of mixing must provide for an effective grinding force such as is supplied, e.g., by a roller mill; here the original, rough pigment dispersion is passed repeatedly between cylinders rotating at different speeds, the clearance betwen the individual "rollers" being so close as to prevent any palpable particles or agglomerates from passing through. Addition to the lipstick mass of a suitable preservative and perfume completes the formula.

The hot lipstick mass is run into molds (of brass or aluminum); when cool, the finished lipsticks are removed from the mold and inserted into their holders.

Because of the emphasis upon an enduring stain, a number of newer, more effective dye solvents have come into partial use in the recent past. Among them are the tetrahydrofurfuryl esters, the propylene glycol monoesters, and the polyethylene glycol ethers. Neverthless, castor oil still retains its dominant position as the essential component of the lipstick base.

Although the use of lipsticks by women is virtually universal, the incidence of lip dermatitis (cheilitis) is comparatively rare. In several instances this dermal reaction has been attributed to the lipstick dyes, and notably to the photosensitizing action of tetrabromofluorescein ("bromoacid"). While this may have been true in the case of certain lipsticks containing only dyes (i.e., without any color lakes) which used to be in vogue some years ago, the opacity of the color lakes employed in modern lipstick formulation may be expected to interfere with the activation of the mechanism of photosensitization. Thus it is more likely that cheilitis, either immediate or after some usage, is due to some other factor, e.g., to the particular individual's intolerance for the lipstick perfume or flavor. In this case, the change to an unperfumed and unflavored lipstick may be the answer.

A different problem is posed by the lipstick of the so-called "deep-staining" type which contains special solvents designed to produce upon the lip an even more intense stain; cases of dryness or irritation have been attributed to this type of lipstick. Therefore, where there is definite reason to suspect the dye as the cause of cheilitis, the use of a "dye-free" lipstick should solve this problem. Such a lipstick (prepared with color lakes alone) will not produce the kind of lasting stain normally expected of either an indelible or a deep-staining lipstick, but it will enable the women to maintain the desired well-groomed appearance.

For the sake of completeness, passing reference is made here to liquid lip colors which are applied with a brush; their position in the cosmetic picture does not approach that of the lipsticks.

EYE MAKE-UP

As pointed out in the initial chapter, the use in the eye area of coal-tar colors in any form is prohibited by the Federal Food, Drug and Cosmetic Act. Accordingly, all eye make-up preparations (mascaras, eyebrow pencils, eyeshadows, etc.) must rely upon approved inert pigments, mostly of inorganic character, for their coloring effects.

Mascara is a popular cosmetic preparation whose function is to darken eye lashes and to give them an appearance of greater length. Its most common form is that of the "cake-mascara"; application is made with a moist brush of special size and construction. Since the base of cake-mascara is of a soap or soap-like character, contact with moisture will emulsify the portion touched, thus permitting its transfer to the eyelashes. Following is an illustrative formula of a cake-mascara:

Mascara

	Per Cent
Triethanolamine stearate	50.0
Carnauba wax	25.0
Paraffin	15.0
Lanolin	5.0
Pigments	5.0
Preservative	q.s.

Depending upon the desired shade the pigments may be drawn from the following categories:

Blue.................... Ultramarine
Green.................... Chromium oxide
Brown.................... Iron oxides (Sienna, Ochre)
Black.................... Carbon black
Violet.................... Ultramarine plus Carmine (NF)

To reduce the color intensity of these pigments, titanium dioxide, an opaque white pigment, may be admixed in the desired proportion. Iridescent effects are obtained by adding finely powdered aluminum (chemically pure grade).

Cream mascara represents a modification of cake mascara in that the hardness of the mass is reduced by the addition of water. This permits filling in tubes and application with a dry brush.

Liquid mascara utilizes an alcoholic rosin solution as its pigment carrying excipient. It appears to have lost its popularity in spite of its more "indelible" character, probably because of its irritant action when placed accidentally in the eye.

Eyebrow pencil is usually furnished to the cosmetic houses by manufacturers of crayons. The pigments are of the same type as employed in mascara.

Eyeshadow is intended to impart "depth" to the eyes by making them appear more prominent against a darker background. A simple formula for a "cream type" of eyeshadow represents a combination of white petrolatum with pigments of the desired shade, e.g., as follows:

Eye Shadow

	Per Cent
Petrolatum U.S.P.	70.0
Mixed pigments	30.0

A variety of shades (blue, green, brown, violet) may be obtained by using some of the several pigments listed before; zinc oxide or titanium dioxide may be added to lighten the shade to the desired degree, and powdered aluminum may be incorporated to obtain an iridescent effect. Grinding to impalpable fineness (e.g., on a roller mill) is a production requirement.

In addition to the cream form, eyeshadow is available also in "stick" form; the "eyeshadow stick" (or "stick eyeshadow") is compounded and produced in a manner entirely similar to that of compounding and producing lipsticks.

NAIL POLISH

A position of importance in grooming, comparable to that of lipsticks, is held by nail polishes (nail lacquers). The formulas of most nail polishes are usually quite complicated; they are guarded as valuable trade secrets. Few, if any, cosmetic firms manufacture their own nail polishes; instead, they are obtaining them from specialty lacquer manufacturers and resell them under their own labels. In the production of nail polish, the lacquer manufacturer draws upon his wide experience in the formulation of other lacquers (e.g., automobile lacquers) to provide a product which would exhibit several desirable characteristics, such as a smooth flow, rapid and uniform drying, and formation of a long lasting film on the nail, resistant to chipping or pealing.

Most nail lacquers contain cellulose nitrate as the film-forming ingredient. In addition there are different solvents, plasticizers, resins and colors. An illustrative formula follows:

Nail Polish Base

	Per Cent
Cellulose nitrate	10.0
Alcohol	5.0
Ethyl and butyl acetates	35.0
Dibutyl phthalate	5.0
Resin, synthetic	10.0
Toluene	35.0

The solvent usually consists of a mixture of chemicals, among which may be acetone, methyl ethyl ketone, one or more alkyl acetates, glycol ethers, alcohols and hydrocarbons, both aromatic (toluene, xylene) and aliphatic (hexane).

The components of the solvent must be present in the correct "balance" so as to provide a proper evaporation rate, also to maintain the integrity of the film while it dries on the nail.

Plasticizers are intended to impart flexibility to what otherwise would be a brittle film of nitrocotton. One of the most widely used plasticizers is dibutyl phthalate; other chemicals with plasticizing action upon nitrocellulose are camphor, castor oil, triphenyl and tricresyl phosphates, dibutyl tartrate and benzyl benzoate.

Resins can be either of natural or of synthetic origin. Their purpose is to impart "body" to the lacquer, also to enhance both the adhesiveness and the luster of the dry film. Ever since the introduction of synthetic resins, the natural resins (such as dammar, mastic, sandarac, etc.) have been losing ground. Among the synthetic resins, the "sulfonamide-formaldehyde" resin is being used quite extensively; it is obtained by reacting p-toluene sulfonamide with formaldehyde at an elevated temperature. Other synthetic resins which are employed in nail polishes are from the vinyl, glyptal, methacrylate, phenolic and other categories.

Most of the observed instances of nail polish dermatitis have been connected with the synthetic resins. Among them were a number of cases of eczematous reactions of the nail bed manifesting a variety of severe symptoms, such as subungual hemorrhages, separation of the distal nail, erythema and edema. The allergic character of the reaction was verified by patch-tests which indicted certain phenol-formaldehyde resins as the principal offending agents. In some instances formaldehyde itself was identified as the causative factor, while the unreacted monomer, methyl methacrylate $H_2C = C(CH_3)\ COOCH_3$, appears to bear the responsibility elsewhere. Yet another case of nail polish dermatitis has been attributed to benzoyl peroxide, a condensing and polymerizing agent which apparently had not been used up completely in the production of the resin. In the recent past, the incidence of nail polish dermatitis has dropped to a very low level.

It is noteworthy that nail polish dermatitis may manifest itself also in areas where its origin is not suspected, e.g., on the eyelids, the cheeks or the neck of the susceptible user; it may occur on a sensitive individual's skin following contact with the enameled nails of another person. Also, a generalized dermatitis has been attributed to the use of nail polish.

Most nail enamels are brightly or even brilliantly colored. The colors are usually insoluble in the lacquer solvent, i.e., they are retained and "fixed" by the enamel film, without actually staining the nail. An exception furnish the clear nail lacquers which often contain very small proportions of soluble dyes. (Of course, all colors employed in the formulation of nail polishes must be selected from the certified listing as required by the Federal Food, Drug, and Cosmetic Act.) "Pastel" shades of nail polish are obtained by the admixture of the inert white pigment, titanium dioxide. Some nail enamels exhibit a "pearly" iridescence which is contributed by a suspension of guanine crystals, obtained originally from the scales of certain species of fish. (There is a report of acquired allergic contact sensitivity to guanine in pearly nail lacquer.)

A nail polish remover may consist simply of one of the more effective solvents (such as acetone or ethyl acetate), or it may represent a mixture of several solvents. Sometimes a small proportion of an oily substance is added with the intent (probably mistaken) to counteract the "drying" action of the solvent. Such an additive may be a true oil (castor oil, olive oil) or a suitable synthetic chemical of oily consistency (butyl stearate, dibutyl phthalate).

For the sake of completeness, brief reference should be made here to the so-called nail "extenders" or "elongators." They produce a hard type of plastic of a nail-like appearance which adheres to the original nail sometimes for several weeks; the application is made over a "guide" which is attached to the tip of the natural fingernail, and the artificial nail "grows" over this guide. Among other things, the preparation (which is mixed immediately prior to application) contains a monomer (e.g., methyl methacrylate) which undergoes rapid polymerization when activated by a suitable catalyst, such as benzoyl or lauroyl peroxide. Incidentally, prior to application, the monomer is protected by an antioxidant (e.g., hydroquinone) against spontaneous polymerization.

That part of the reaction which has to do with the polymerization of the monomer with formation of the methacrylate plastic, may be described as follows:

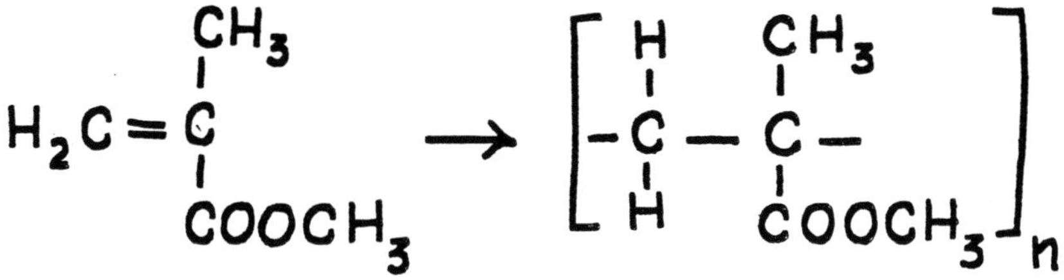

$$H_2C{=}\underset{\underset{COOCH_3}{|}}{\overset{\overset{CH_3}{|}}{C}} \longrightarrow \left[-\underset{\underset{H}{|}}{\overset{\overset{H}{|}}{C}} - \underset{\underset{COOCH_3}{|}}{\overset{\overset{CH_3}{|}}{C}} - \right]_n$$

This type of product was involved in a dermatological problem which is not too surprising in view of the fact that its application is likely to place potential sensitizers (methyl methacrylate, benzoyl peroxide, hydroquinone) in direct contact with the skin.

Among the other nail preparations of significant usage are the cuticle softeners (removers). They are formulated either with alkalies (e.g., 2 to 5 per cent of potassium hydroxide) or with alkaline salts (e.g., 5 to 10 per cent of sodium carbonate or trisodium phosphate) as active ingredients. By causing a partial hydrolysis and swelling of keratin they facilitate removal of the eponychium, which is done either by cutting, or pushing it back with a suitable wooden or metal implement.

The high alkalinity of this type of product creates a risk of dermatitis. This is why some less alkaline preparations are also available which are based upon certain alkyl amines (e.g., triethanolamine, isopropanolamine); however, their performance may not be quite as efficient as that of the more alkaline formulations.

Chapter 7

ANTIPERSPIRANTS AND DEODORANTS

OF THE TWO FORMS OF PERSPIRATION, *viz.*, the sensible and the insensible, only the former is involved in the creation of a cosmetic problem, particularly with regard to its secretion in the axillary area.

Eccrine sweat collected by capillary attraction does not develop any malodor on standing. However, when obtained, e.g., by guiding the edge of a test tube with pressure over the skin, a sweat specimen develops odor; this is due to the degradation of some biological matter (keratin, sebum) by microorganisms transferred from the skin surface to the sample of sweat collected in this fashion. By contrast, secreted apocrine sweat itself carries the kind of organic material (of both protein and lipid character) which is susceptible to microbial degradation with formation of volatile malodorous substances. Since the apocrine glands are abundant in the axillary area (in association with eccrine glands), the perspiratory malodor from this source is particularly noticeable and objectionable.

The essential role of microorganisms in producing the malodor of perspiration is also confirmed by the experimental finding that mixed, freshly collected perspiration which had been passed through a Berkefeld assembly remained free from odor upon standing, while an unfiltered specimen quickly developed a strong odor, and, incidentally, its pH changed from acid to alkaline.

ANTIPERSPIRANTS

The formulation of an antiperspirant calls for the use of an astringent chemical capable of reducing the flow of perspiration. Although the relevant reaction mechanism continues to be controversial, it may be assumed that it involves the sorption of such a chemical (e.g., aluminum salt) by certain cutaneous (mostly keratinous) proteins (possibly accompanied by an edema around the lumen of the sweat duct which effects its constriction; as a result, the flow of perspiration would be impeded and its volume reduced). It is also known that hardly any aluminum reaches the area of the dermis; this would be an argument against the view that alteration of the physiological activity of the sweat glands is involved in the antiperspirant mechanism of hydrolyzing metal salts.

While a number of metal salts have the capacity of interacting with proteins, most cosmetic antiperspirant preparations employ aluminum compounds as their active ingredients. The use of zirconium compounds, which had begun to gain some popularity in recent years, has declined again following the publication of reports which attribute the incidence of axillary granulomas to the use of "sodium zirconium lactate," actually sodium hydrogen trilactozirconylate, $Na_2H_2ZrO(C_3H_4O_3)_3$, as active ingredient of certain formulas. This reaction has been established as being of an allergic character; cross-sensitization phenomena have not been encountered. It should be mentioned, however, that granuloma formation is not a problem with zirconium oxychloride $ZrOCl_2$, which has an entirely acceptable record of fitness for use in antiperspirant formulations. In this connection, it will be noted that in zirconium oxychloride, the zirconium atom occurs as the cation, whereas in sodium zirconium lactate it is present in the anionic portion of the molecule. No doubt, this difference in the ionic character of the metal is at the basis of the different behavior of the two zirconium compounds under consideration.

Other potentially effective polyvalent metal salts are not being employed in the formulation of antiperspirants, either because of their capacity to produce some undesirable collateral reactions (e.g., discoloration of the skin or fabrics by chromic or ferric salts), or because of their transcutaneous toxicity (e.g., in the case of mercuric salts).

As for the anion portion of suitable aluminum salts, the chloride, the sulfate, the chlorohydrate (also known as the chlorhydroxide), the sulfamate, the phosphate and the phenolsulfonate are represented most frequently, although some others such as the lactate, the acetotartrate and the methionate are encountered in actual usage, or mentioned in published (patent) references.

The proportion of an aluminum salt in an antiperspirant formulation is usually within the range of 10 to 20 per cent.

A simple type of a liquid antiperspirant is illustrated by the following formula:

Antiperspirant

	Per Cent
Aluminum chloride	15.0
Propylene glycol	5.0
Water	80.0

(The propylene glycol contributes a measure of humectant action which counteracts crystallization of the aluminum salt, e.g., in the nozzle of a spray applicator. For the sake of speeding up the evaporation after application, a part of the water may be replaced by alcohol).

While possessed of considerable efficacy in reducing the output of axillary perspiration, such a formula (although representative of a commercial product) is not altogether desirable because of its comparatively high potential for skin irritation and fabric corrosion.

This potential is a function of the acidity of the solution which is generated by the hydrolysis of the aluminum chloride according to:

$$AlCl_3 + 3H_2O \rightleftharpoons Al(OH)_3 + 3HCl$$

If left unchecked, the high acidity of an aluminum chloride solution could irritate some skins, particularly upon repeated application. And as to its effect upon fabrics (notably those of linen, cotton or viscose rayon), prolonged or repeated exposure to this acidity will cause their gradual rotting. However, maximum irreversible fabric damage is produced at the high temperature of ironing, if the garment is subjected to it directly, i.e., without prior laundering.

The great practical significance of the last-named problem accounts for the considerable number of formulations which have been developed to overcome this difficulty. These formulations may be divided broadly into two categories, *viz.*, those which contain added inhibitory or "buffering" agents designed to reduce the high acidity of the hydrolyzing salts, and those which depend upon certain metal compounds as active ingredients which generate a lower degree of acidity, i.e., without the aid of any added modifiers.

One of the modifying agents suitable for the former type of formulation is urea (carbamide). In the following simple combination:

Antiperspirant (Buffered)

	Per Cent
Aluminum chloride	15.0
Urea	5.0
Propylene glycol	5.0
Water	75.0

urea reduces the acidity of the formula at room temperature by bonding; at higher temperatures, such as those produced in the course of ironing, its protective action against heat-activated corrosive acidity is probably enhanced by the liberation of ammonia.

A simple formula for a liquid antiperspirant of the second type might read as follows:

Antiperspirant (Buffered)

	Per Cent
Aluminum chlorohydrate	15.0
Propylene glycol	5.0
Water	80.0

This formula does not require a modifier since its active agent, aluminum chlorohydrate (chlorhydroxide), does not produce the degree of acidity generated by aluminum chloride.

While the above examples represent "liquid" antiperspirant preparations, a wide variety of antiperspirants are available also in "cream" and in "lotion" forms.

Both these varieties call for the use of acid-stable emulsions as excipients (since the acidity of the hydrolyzing aluminum salt would "break" an emulsion containing, e.g., an alkali or ammonium stearate as emulsifying agent). Accordingly, acid-stable anionic and nonionic emulsifiers are employed in the formulation of antiperspirant creams and lotions. Among representative examples of suitable anionic emulsifiers are sodium and triethanolamine lauryl sulfate or sodium alkyl sulfonate, while some of the hexitol esters (Tweens) and their polyoxyethylene ethers (Spans) are examples of nonionic emulsifiers.

Following is a simple illustrative formula of an antiperspirant cream based upon a nonionic type of emulsion, with a "self-buffered" active ingredient (aluminum chlorhydroxide):

Antiperspirant Cream

	Per Cent
Stearic acid	15.0
Sorbitan monostearate (Span 60)	5.0
Polyoxyethylene sorbitan monostearate (Tween 60)	5.0
Aluminum chlorhydroxide	20.0
Water	55.0

This type of formula may be produced also in liquid ("lotion") form, by reducing the proportion of stearic acid (with a corresponding increase in that of water), and incorporating a suitable emulsifying principle to insure stability of the liquid emulsion. Some of the "roll-on" dispensers available commercially are charged with this type of preparation.

Antiperspirant properties may be imparted also to other forms of carriers (e.g., powders, sticks), but the role of such preparations is of a comparatively lesser importance.

ANTIBACTERIAL AND DEODORANT ACTION OF ANTIPERSPIRANTS

It should be mentioned, at this point, that antiperspirant preparations are also deodorant in action probably because of their degree of acidity which appears to be sufficient to control the multiplication and activity of odor-causing skin bacteria. Since simple mechanical cleansing of the axillary fossae is not effective in suppressing the tendency to perspiratory malodor for any appreciable period of time, the conclusion is justified that of the two types of bacterial skin flora, *viz.*, "transient" and "resident," it is the latter that plays the major role here.

The following microorganisms have been identified routinely in the swabbing of the axillae of healthy men: *Staphylococcus aureus* and *albus*, *Corynebacteria*, *Aerobacter aerogenes* and *Sarcina lutea*. These microorganisms do not grow at a pH of 4.5 or lower; since the hydrolyzing aluminum salt of an antiperspirant preparation usually develops an acidity of this, or of a greater intensity, inhibitory action upon skin bacteria should be evident in the absence of any special bacteriostatic agent. This has been confirmed experimentally in several instances.

Deodorants (Without Antiperspirant Action)

Since control of perspiratory malodor depends essentially upon the control of bacterial activity, topical application of suitable antiseptics (to the primary areas of odor-forming secretion, such as the axillary fossae) should reduce or suppress such odors by reducing or suppressing bacterial proliferation and biological activity, but without affecting the flow of perspiration. While different antiseptics might lend themselves for this purpose, hexachlorophene (2,2′-methylenebis[3,4,6-trichlorophenol]) established itself early in this field, followed by bithionol (2,2′-thiobis [4,6-dichlorophenol]), and others in the more recent past. Relevant is the observation that hexachlorophene prevented apocrine sweat *in vitro* from developing odor on standing, and that regular washing of one axilla with a hexachlorophene bearing detergent provided significant odor protection, as compared with the odorous condition of the other, the control axilla; also, that hair clipped from the treated axilla was found upon plating and incubation to be substantially free from bacteria, in contradistinction to hair removed from the control axilla.

Deodorants operating on the antibacterial principle alone (i.e., without antiperspirant action) may be produced in different application forms, such as creams, lotions or powders. However, one of the more popular forms is that of a "deodorant stick" in which alcohol, solidified by means of sodium stearate, is the vehicle for the antiseptic agent. Following is an illustrative formula:

Deodorant Stick

	Per Cent
Sodium stearate	8.0
Sorbitol	5.0
Hexachlorophene	.2
Alcohol	80.0
Water	6.8

To make this type of product, the sodium stearate is dissolved in the warm mixture of the other ingredients, and the clear liquid is poured into molds where it congeals. Slight pressure exerted upon the application of the "deodorant stick" causes a small quantity of the solution to spread on the skin where the antibacterial agent is deposited after the evaporation of the solvent.

As indicated above, antiseptic substances acting as deodorants are generally devoid of antiperspirant action. An exception to this rule is being claimed for quaternary ammonium antiseptics (e.g., benzalkonium chloride) which are credited with a capacity for inhibiting the delivery of eccrine sweat to the skin surface; this effect is said to depend upon the existence of an electrophysiologic potential along the sweat duct.

Only brief reference to "chlorophyll" is justified here. Originally, a unique claim had been advanced for one of its derivatives (chlorophyllin) to the effect that its oral ingestion would reduce or eliminate body odor; but several independent investigators were unsuccessful in their attempt to obtain experimental support for this claim. On the other hand, if chlorophyllin is brought into direct contact with certain types of odorous matter (e.g., in purulent infections) deodorant action is noted. However, to be effective in a deodorant cosmetic, its concentration probably would have to be so high as to stain the skin and clothes.

Another principle which reached a discussion stage recently (if not yet one of large-scale usage) is that of deodorization by means of certain ion-exchange resins. Their effect is attributed to the adsorption of odorous substances by systems of paired resins (i.e., from both the cation and the anion categories). When such material (in finely powdered form) is incorporated (at the rate of 20 per cent) in a suitable ointment, emulsion or mucilage, the deodorant effectiveness is greater than if it were applied directly, e.g., by dusting the axillary area.

In spite of authoritative exhortation, some cosmetic houses have seen fit to employ certain antibiotics in the formulation of deodorants. Among them are tyrothricin and neomycin, which applied topically are claimed to exert prolonged control of odor-causing bacteria.

Dermatitis caused by antiperspirants is localized in the axillary area, as a rule. Here it may appear either as a vesicular erythematous eruption or as folliculitis. Its direct cause resides probably in the distinctly acid character of the type of product under discussion; its incidence and severity should depend, therefore, to some extent upon the degree of acidity generated by hydrolysis, particularly in the case of a formulation devoid of any buffering system. Skin macerated by moisture or abraded by shaving, is subject to irritation which may be intensified by the presence of an anionic surfactant such as employed in the formulation of an antiperspirant cream or lotion.

Primary irritation, rather than sensitization is usually involved in the etiology of axillary dermatitis brought about by antiperspirants; however, a sensitization reaction (e.g., due to the perfume used to scent the antiperspirant or deodorant cosmetic) should not be discounted as a possible factor in certain instances.

Chapter 8

HAIR DRESSINGS AND TONICS

THE GROOMING AIDS in this category occur in a variety of forms. The *brilliantines* are essentially of an oily character, consisting of perfumed (sometimes tinted) mineral, vegetable or synthetic oils, or their mixtures in varying proportions. *Solid brilliantines* are of essentially the same character as their liquid counterparts except that they are of a stiffer consistency, which is achieved by the incorporation of petrolatum, paraffin, ceresin, lanolin, beeswax or any combination of them. Both types are intended to control unruly (or kinky) hair, and to impart to it a glossy appearance.

	Liquid Brilliantine Per Cent	*Solid Brilliantine* Per Cent
Mineral oil	75.0	50.0
Isopropyl myristate	25.0	—
Petrolatum	—	40.0
Paraffin	—	10.0

To reduce the greasy quality such as shown by most brilliantines, the *"two-layer"* preparations are compounded with diluted alcohol and a suitable oil, the latter forming a separate phase. This type of cosmetic is applied to the hair following agitation of the bottle which causes a temporary emulsion to form. An illustrative formula follows:

Hair Dressing

	Per Cent
Mineral oil	25.0
Alcohol	25.0
Water	50.0

Hair dressings are produced also in the form of true (oil-in-water or water-in-oil) emulsions according to the principles considered previously. A simple (O/W) "cream dressing" might show the following composition:

Hair Dressing

	Per Cent
Mineral oil	25.0
Beeswax	5.0
Triethanolamine stearate	5.0
Water	65.0

A cold cream formula might double as a W/O type of cream dressing.

A special position is being held by *hair tonics* which, at one time, were represented as cures for a variety of scalp disorders, including alopecia, dandruff, etc. Modern preparations in this category are scented and tinted hydro-alcoholic solutions usually containing rubefacient and antiseptic ingredients, the former designed to intensify the capillary blood flow, the latter to control "scalp odor" of microbial origin. Among the common rubefacients are the tinctures of cantharides, capsicum, jaborandi and cinchona, also quinine, pilocarpine and certain tars (e.g., those of pine, birch or cade). The antiseptics are usually from the class of phenol derivatives, and may include p-chloro-m-xylenol, thymol and chlorothymol, beta-naphthol, resorcinol and its monoacetate, salicylic acid, and others. Considerable discretion is required in the formulation of hair tonics so as to avoid the risk of reaching irritant concentrations. By the same token, dermatitis from hair tonics is more frequent than from other hair-grooming preparations.

"Bay rum" contains oil of bay and Jamaican rum as ingredients.

Following is an illustrative formula of a hair tonic:

Hair Tonic

	Per Cent
Resorcinol monoacetate	3.0
Tincture of capsicum	5.0
Mixed essential oils (bay, cinnamon leaf, cloves)	.5
Alcohol	75.0
Water	16.5

Chapter 9

HAIR WAVING

THE CRAVING FOR CURLY HAIR is at least as old as recorded history, and probably older. There is a direct conncetion between the ancient Egyptian method of hair-waving (by winding the hair on wooden sticks, covering it with Nile mud, and baking it in the sun) and the more modern heat-waving processes which combine the physical effect of heat (generated either by electricity or by some exothermic reaction) with the chemical effect upon the hair of a suitable alkaline substance (borax, sodium carbonate, sodium phosphate, etc.).

Although heat-waving of hair has maintained its popularity for many decades, virtually all hair waving is being done nowadays by means of the "cold-wave" process which first made its appearance some twenty-five years ago.

While the chemistry of cold-waving may not have been elucidated completely, there is general agreement as to the events occurring in the several steps involved.

Human hair keratin is a protein characterized by a high proportion of cystine. The keratin fibers are assumed to consist of polypeptide chains cross-linked by several different types of bonds among which the "disulfide" bond *via* the cystine grouping is considered responsible for the elastic quality of normal hair. Rupture of the disulfide bond abolishes this elasticity and deprives the hair of its tendency to maintain its normal "shape". However, if straight hair which has been rendered limp in this fashion is wound on a curler, and then treated chemically so as to reconstruct the disulfide linkage, the concomitant restoration of its elastic quality will cause it to acquire the new, curled shape.

Although different mercaptans have been considered at one time or another, ammonium thioglycolate is being used almost exclusively as the means of splitting the disulfide linkage of the keratin while the hair is wound on the curler. This involves a reductive process in the course of which two cysteine residues are formed out of one cystine residue. Reconstitution of the cystine bond is effected by oxidation of the sulfhydryl groups to the corresponding disulfide. Following is an illustration of the probable reaction scheme ("Ker" is the keratin residue):

$$Ker_1 \langle {}^{CO}_{NH} \rangle CH-CH_2-S-S-CH_2\,HC \langle {}^{CO}_{NH} \rangle Ker_2 \rightleftharpoons$$

$$\rightleftharpoons Ker_1 \langle {}^{CO}_{NH} \rangle CH-CH_2-SH + HS-CH_2-HC \langle {}^{CO}_{NH} \rangle Ker_2$$

Among the oxidizing agents most frequently used for this purpose are sodium bromate, sodium perborate and hydrogen peroxide; these chemicals are designated (popularly but incorrectly) as "neutralizers." There exists also a process in which atmospheric oxygen is utilized to bring about such oxidation, with a manganous salt serving as the catalyst.

The pH of a cold waving lotion should lie between 8.5 and 9.5; at a pH of 8 or below, little or no waving action is obtained, while at a pH of 10 or above, a depilating effect may manifest itself.

Below is an illustrative formula of a simple cold-waving solution:

Cold Waving Solution

	Per Cent
Thioglycolic acid	5.75
Ammonia (26%)	2.00
Water, dist.	93.25

As a rule a small percentage of a surfactant is added to promote a more rapid and uniform wetting of the hair.

Following is a brief description of the hair waving process:

The shampooed hair, while still damp, is divided into the desired number of sections, and each section is wound on an individual curler. The "waving lotion" is now applied to the point of saturation of the hair. The duration of contact will depend upon the type of hair, as well as upon the desired kind ("tightness") of the curl. After a thorough rinse which should remove most of the unused thioglycolate, the hair is treated with the "neutralizer" (oxidizer) whose function it is not only to reconstitute the cystine bonds of the hair keratin, but also to inactivate any of the unreacted thioglycolate. At this point the curlers are removed, revealing the new, "wavy" appearance of the hair.

Generally speaking, cold waving preparations have not created any toxicological or dermatological problems, in spite of their very extensive usage. This fact is supported by the results of toxicological investigations with rats and guinea pigs, as well as by studies on cutaneous irritation and sensitization performed on human beings. Some incidence of dermatitis attributed to this type of product might have resulted either from misuse (e.g., failure to follow directions), or from an improper formulation encountered in an occasional package, (e.g., too high a concentration of ammonia acting as a primary irritant). However, prolonged contact with a cold waving solution, such as would occur in the course of a cold waving operation in a hair-dressing establishment, would certainly call for the protection of the operator's hands by rubber gloves.

Damage to the hair (breaking) may be caused either by a formulation which is stronger than required, or by an excessively long processing period. In any case, such damage is transitory in character as its effect is limited to the hair shaft, and no inhibition of hair growth is observable.

To overcome the objectionable odor of ammonia, also to reduce the risk of irritancy, certain alkanolamines (such as monoethanolamine) are being used either in partial or total replacement of ammonia in some more recent formulations.

HAIR STRAIGHTENERS

Another related type of hair product is the hair straightener. The modern hair straightener used to smooth out kinky (Negroid) hair operates on the same principle as the cold wave. Indeed, this type of hair-straightening by means of a thioglycolate treatment may be regarded as a "wave-in-reverse."

However, in addition to thioglycolate straighteners, there still exist preparations which are designed to act mechanically by "plastering down" the hair with the aid of a suitable adhesive substance, such as gum karaya. Other mechanically acting agents contain petrolatum, usually in combination with paraffin or ozokerite.

The "hot comb" is used particularly in beauty parlors, in conjunction with preparations of the petrolatum variety in a treatment termed "hair pressing."

Finally, there is the "alkaline straightener" which may contain from five to ten percent of sodium hydroxide incorporated in a stearate ("vanishing cream") base. As might be expected, this type of product requires extreme care in application (which includes protection of the skin along the hair line by means of a layer of petrolatum) in order to prevent an alkali burn. Fortunately, this strongly alkaline product is being replaced rapidly by the thioglycolate type of hair straightener.

WAVE SETS

In addition to permanent waving preparations there exist numerous wave-setting formulas, usually representing solutions or dispersions of certain gums or mucilages such as gum karaya, gum tragacanth, quince seed, sodium alginate, pectin and the like, either in individual or in combined form. When applied to hair wound on a curler and permitted to dry, this type of preparation leaves a film which forces the hair to retain the shape given it by winding.

In another category of wave-setting agents are the hair lacquers or hair sprays previously formulated with shellac, but nowadays based mostly upon polyvinyl pyrrolidone in alcoholic or hydroalcoholic solution.

The effects of all such preparations are of a comparatively short duration, as compared with those of thioglycolate waves.

Below is an illustrative formula of a hair lacquer:

Hair Lacquers

	Per Cent
Polyvinyl pyrrolidone (PVP)	2.50
Alcohol	20.00
Sorbitol	5.00
Water	72.50
Preservative	q.s.

Sorbitol is added as a humectant to counteract any flaking tendency of the dry film. Preparations of this type also contain some perfume and preservative. Sometimes a silicone is added for the sake of water repellency.

Hair lacquers are frequently formulated for application as aerosols by combination with suitable propellents in pressurized packages.

HAIR RINSES

Until comparatively recently, acidic solutions (such as lemon juice, vinegar) have been used for rinsing the hair after shampooing. The primary purpose of such a rinse is to react with any lime soap precipitated on the hair, thereby facilitating the removal of its dulling film.

The modern hair rinse serves a different purpose, *viz.*, to produce an extremely thin film on the hair in order to counteract its matting and to make it more manageable (for combing, etc.). Such a film is produced usually by adsorption of a substantive quaternary ammonium surfactant (e.g., stearyl dimethyl benzyl ammonium chloride); other suitable chemicals may be drawn from the class of alkanolamids of long-chain fatty acids. Although an aqueous solution of such a substance would be satisfactory for the purpose under consideration, the preparations on the market usually occur in the form of emulsions designed to create the idea of greater benefit for the hair, as would be associated with the image of a liquid cream; hence the frequent designation of "cream rinse" for this type of product.

In compounding a hair rinse with a quaternary ammonium salt, care must be exercised in the judicious selection of a proper chemical, since it is known that in the concentrations employed (3 to 5 per cent), some representatives of this class could act as skin or eye irritants.

Chapter 10

EPILATION AND DEPILATION

ALTHOUGH A SHARP distinction between "epilation" and "depilation" is not being made generally, it is felt that the term "epilation" should be reserved for the physical removal of the substantially intact hair, whereas "depilation" should be applied to those procedures designed to remove unwanted hair which depend upon a partial chemical degradation of the hair keratin and resultant weakening of the hair structure.

Both epilation and depilation are being practiced very widely. While this is not the place to discuss epilation by electrolysis or by x-ray, some reference should be made here to mechanical epilation by means of an epilatory "wax" of which the following is an illustrative example:

Epilatory Wax

	Per Cent
Rosin	50.0
Beeswax	25.0
Paraffin	15.0
Petrolatum	10.0

This "wax" is applied to the hirsute area in a melted form, and allowed to solidify on cooling, thereby entrapping the protruding hairs. A quick pull at the edge of the coating peals off the wax which now pulls out the hair caught in the epilatory mass. This operation must be carried out skillfully and quickly in order to prevent pain and to assure success.

Needless to add, the epilatory mixture must be compounded so as to permit application in melted form at a sufficiently low temperature to prevent burning; on the other hand, it must be able to set on the skin to a sufficiently rigid yet pliable consistency so as to permit pulling off without breaking and without permitting the enmeshed hairs to slide out.

Some epilatory preparations are applied over a strip of gauze, rather than directly to the skin; others are produced in a form resembling an adhesive plaster.

Chemicals other than those listed in the illustrative example have been used occasionally in formulating epilatory compositions; among them are honey, molasses, also crude rubber dissolved in a suitable solvent which volatilizes upon application to the skin.

Chemical depilatories enjoy a much greater popularity than the "wax" type epilatories. At one time, the alkali and alkali-earth sulfides were being used exclusively as dehairing agents, although other chemicals, such as the (alkaline) stannites, were suggested for this purpose from time to time. The thallium depilatories (based on thallium acetate as a rule) which made their appearance some fifty years ago, were not true depilatories since they did not act chemically upon the hair keratin; instead, their effectiveness depended upon an easier removal of the hair from the follicle. At any rate, their systemic toxicity, similar to that of the mercury salts, was responsible for their virtual abandonment.

Most depilatories sold nowadays employ, as active principle, calcium thioglycolate in a controlled alkaline medium (pH 12 to 12.5). They occur usually in the form of pastes or creams which may contain up to 15 per cent of calcium thioglycolate usually in combination with suitable inorganic and organic fillers and "bodying" ingredients to yield an emulsified product of the desired consistency and ease of application.

Following is a sample formula of a "depilatory cream":

Depilatory Cream

	Per Cent
Calcium thioglycolate	7.5
Calcium carbonate	20.0
Calcium hydroxide	1.5
Titanium dioxide	1.0
Cetyl alcohol	5.0
Sodium lauryl sulfate	0.5
Sodium silicate (42.5 Bé.)	3.0
Water	61.5

In the above formula, calcium hydroxide and sodium silicate furnish the desired alkalinity; the latter yields also a measure of protection of collapsible metal containers (tubes) against a chemical attack by the alkaline cream.

Cetyl alcohol emulsified with the aid of sodium lauryl sulfate is intended to supply some emollient action, and to minimize skin irritation.

Generally speaking, thioglycolate depilatories, when used according to directions, do not give rise to any persistent dermal reactions. In the very small number of reported dermatoses attributed to them, the effect was probably one of primary irritation, rather than of sensitization, although the possibility of allergic reactions is not to be discounted completely.

Chapter 11

HAIR DYES

ESSENTIALLY, there are three types of "permanent" hair dyes, *viz.*, vegetable, metallic and synthetic-organic.

Vegetable Hair Dyes

Vegetable dyes are obtained from the various portions of different plant materials. One such hair dye is henna; although its history dates back to Egypt's third dynasty, it is still in extensive use today.

The henna plant, *Lawsonia inermis* L., is a shrub which grows not only in Egypt, but also in India, Iran, Tunis, and in other tropical countries. Only the leaves and stems are gathered; after drying, they are ground up to an impalpable powder.

When applied to the hair in the form of an aqueous infusion (henna pack), as a rinse, or in a shampoo, henna imparts to the hair a characteristic reddish color. (The fingernails are stained, too, unless the hands are protected by rubber gloves.) The coloring principle is 2-hydroxy-1,4-naphthoquinone (lawsone), an orange-red dye substantive for keratin.

The principal disadvantage of henna is the rather unnatural shade of hair it produces. This is why it is combined occasionally in varying proportions with powdered indigo (*Indigofera argentea*) leaves ("reng") in order to produce a series of shades from light brown to black.

Another vegetable hair "dye" is camomile; particularly the "Roman", German and Hungarian varieties of camomile are in demand. The coloring effect is provided by apigenin (4′,5,7-trihydroxyflavone), both in its free form and as a glucoside.

Camomile, too, may be applied as a pack, rinse or shampoo, sometimes in combination with henna to modify the shade produced by either colorant alone.

Other vegetable materials still are, or have been used for hair dyeing, mostly in some European and Oriental countries. Thus, the green walnut shells yield juglone (5-hydroxy-1,4-naphthoquinone) as a brown coloring agent, while nutgalls (pathological excrescences on the leaves of the white oak) are rich in gallic acid and tannin; the latter are employed, among other things, in the production of "rastik," an ancient hair dye still in vogue in the Orient, and made originally by roasting nutgalls with copper and iron filings. A paste prepared from this mixture is applied to the hair. The metal salts formed in the course of the process contribute a "mordant" effect; upon reaction with tannin and gallic acid (pyrogallol) a deep black color is produced.

Metallic Hair Colorants

Preparations falling within this category are referred to in commerce as "color restorers," rather than as hair dyes.

The application of *lead* to "restore" color on gray hair was practiced in ancient Rome with the aid of lead combs dipped in vinegar. The lead acetate thus formed reacts progressively with the sulfur components of hair keratin by reduction to lower insoluble oxidation stages and by forming insoluble sulfides; its prolonged exposure on the hair to light and air is also involved in this type of reaction. The insoluble metal compounds deposited on the hair shaft are held fast by the imbrications of the cuticle scales.

Lead is still being used nowadays as a color restorer, albeit in a different manner. It is applied in the form of a mixture of lead acetate and sodium thiosulfate ($Na_2S_2O_3$), as shown by the following formula:

"Color Restorer"

Lead acetate	0.5
Sodium thiosulfate	1.5
Propylene glycol	10.0
Water	88.0

Lead color restorers are also available in "two-bottle" sets containing dilute solutions (e.g., 2 per cent of lead acetate and sodium sulfite respectively), to be combined immediately prior to application. Some newer two-bottle combinations feature a thioglycolate instead of a sulfite; the former's greater reactivity tends to accelerate the "coloring" process.

The *silver* color restorer (usually ammoniacal silver nitrate) is applied, as a rule, in combination with a suitable "developer," *viz.*, a reducing agent, such as pyrogallol. Depending upon the hair shade desired (i.e., from blond to black) different concentrations of silver nitrate and of pyrogallol are employed, (e.g., from 1 to 15 per cent of ammoniacal silver nitrate, and from 1 to 5 per cent of pyrogallol.)

It is noteworthy that there are no well authenticated reports either of plumbism or of argyria attributed to routine use of lead or silver hair preparations, respectively; nor does the Food and Drug Administration place any restriction upon their use.

For the sake of completeness, it should be added that metal salts other than those of lead and silver have been utilized in the formulation of hair colors. The series includes various salts of bismuth, manganese, iron, cobalt, nickel, cadmium and tin.

Oxidation Hair Dyes

By far the most important position in the hair dyeing field is occupied by certain synthetic organic chemicals, usually referred to as oxidation hair dyes. Actually, these chemicals are dye intermediates (combined with "modifiers") which upon application to the hair with concomitant oxidation produce a permanent color. In view of the tremendous popularity of this hair coloring principle it is noteworthy that the fundamental studies on permanent coloring of fur, feathers and hair were carried out some eighty years ago in France and in Germany. Originally only para-phenylenediamine was employed as the principal dye intermediate; gradually numerous other chemicals came into use, both as intermediates and as modifiers, permitting production of the wide range of shades available today.

As a "permanent hair dye," this type of preparation is put up usually in a two-container package, one holding the intermediate mixture, the other an oxidizing agent, such as hydrogen peroxide, sodium perborate, etc. The basic substance must be capable of changing to a quinonoid structure as a result of oxidation. The initial stages of the reaction commencing with p-phenylenediamine are:

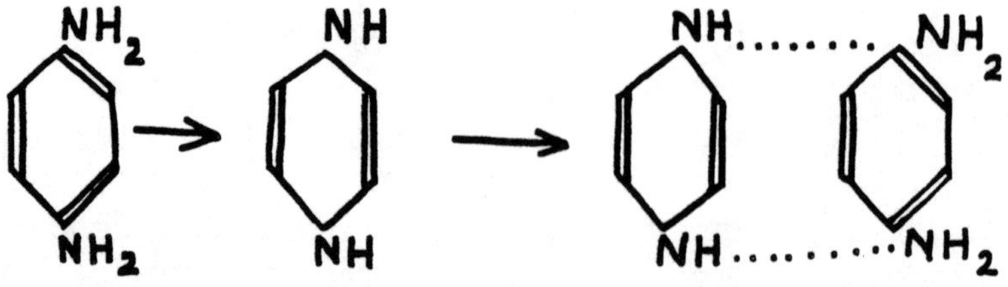

p-Phenylenediamine *p-Quinonediimine* *Quinhydrone*

Quinhydrone, the third stage of the above scheme is not the final coloring agent. Actually, the reaction progresses further with formation of insoluble azine derivatives through structural participation of certain reactive groups of the hair keratin molecule within the cortex as well as on the surface of the hair; the latter factor is involved in the "permanence" of the hair tint produced.

Among the benzenoid chemicals capable of undergoing the change to a quinonoid structure which are employed in the formulation of oxidation hair dyes are p-toluylene diamine, 2,4-diaminoanisole, o- and p-aminophenol, 2,4-diaminophenol, 2-nitro-p-phenylenediamine and others. Simple combinations of such intermediates with shade modifiers are illustrated by the following formulas for two hair shades:

Hair Dyes

	Blond	*Chestnut*
p-Phenylenediamine	0.30	2.00
o-Aminophenol	0.15	0.20
p-Aminophenol	—	0.20
p-Methylaminophenol sulfate	0.50	0.15
4-Nitro-o-phenylenediamine	—	0.15
2-Nitro-p-phenylenediamine	—	0.15
p-Aminodiphenylamine	0.15	0.20
Resorcinol	0.25	1.00
Pyrocatechol	0.25	—
Pyrogallol	0.30	—
Sodium sulfite	0.30	0.30
Base, q.s.	100.00	100.00

It will be noted that the above formulas specify sodium sulfite. This chemical is intended to act as an antioxidant, i.e., to counteract progressive oxidative deterioration of the product while on the shelf or awaiting application to the hair.

The "base" mentioned as the last item is a suitable mixture of substances designed to promote uniform distribution of the preparation upon the hair. Its composition may vary from that of a simple solvent (e.g., 50 per cent alcohol) to a combination of emulsifying agents, the latter type of base being found especially in the so-called "shampoo tints."

It is of interest that following their introduction and for some time thereafter, the oxidation hair dyes based upon p-phenylenediamine were threatened with condemnation by health authorities, both here and abroad, because of the frequency and the severity of dermal reactions caused by them. Eventually the attacks ceased when increasing purity of the chemicals employed in formulation plus correct procedure in application caused a sharp decline in the number of complaints. Nevertheless, Federal law provides for a mandatory, specifically worded cautionary statement on the labels of oxidation hair dyes, emphasizing the risk of skin irritation and requiring the performance of a preliminary test to establish absence of allergic sensitivity that might give rise to extensive dermatitis in the individual case. Expressly forbidden is the application of this dyeing principle to eyebrows or eyelashes because of the risk of blindness.

There are experimental data in support of the hypothesis that oxidation products of p-phenylenediamine (rather than this chemical itself) are involved in sensitization reactions. The view has been expressed that quinonediimine can serve as a coupling component to link with epidermal proteins which are thereby converted into antigens.

In this connection it is of interest that the ortho- and meta-isomers of phenylenediamine were found to be non-reactive in individuals exhibiting sensitivity to the para-isomer. The probable reason is that in the latter case the antigenicity resides in the para-quinonoid (rather than in the benzenoid) stage which the former isomers are incapable of producing.

There is also the possibility that allergic dermatitis produced by p-phenylenediamine may be the result, in some instances, of cross-sensitization with structurally (immunochemically) related primary allergens, such as benzocaine or procaine, (also sulfonamides, antihistamines and azo-dyes). This relationship is illustrated by the following formulas (see next page).

Other hair dyes exhibit little, if any, potential for allergic sensi-

NH_2	NH_2	NH_2	NH_2
NH_2	$COOC_2H_5$	$COOC_2H_4N(C_2H_5)_2$	SO_2NH_2
p-Phenylenediamine	*Benzocaine*	*Procaine*	*Sulfanilamide*

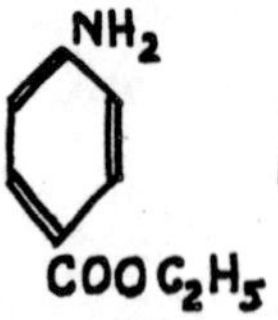

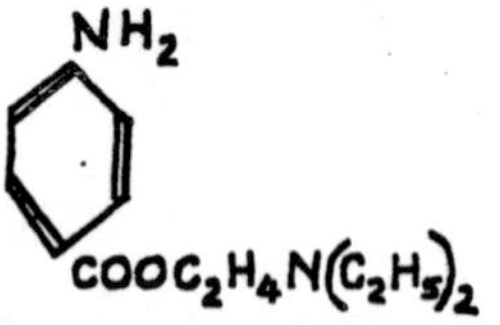

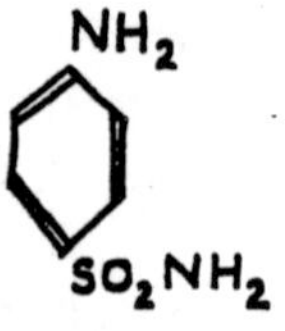

tization. This is true not only of henna, but also of the progressive type of "dyes" based on heavy metal salts.

The same appears to be true of the newer types of hair coloring preparations which employ true stains, often selected from the list of the so-called F, D and C colors, i.e., those enjoying regulatory sanction for use in foods, drugs or cosmetics. These dyes are used in the formulation of "color rinses" which produce only temporary color effects and require renewal after one or more shampooings. Special rinses intended to neutralize the unattractive yellowish tinge of gray hair are based upon suitable blue dyes, such as methylene blue.

Hair Bleaches

Hydrogen peroxide is used most frequently to lighten the natural shade of the hair. Three to six per cent solutions of H_2O_2 are used, as a rule, for this purpose; a small quantity of ammonia is added as activator. To produce the "platinum blond" effect, the hair is bleached first to its lightest shade, and the residual yellowish tinge is "neutralized" by careful rinsing with a solution of a suitable blue dye.

The term "white henna" is a misnomer since the substance sold under this designation consists of magnesium carbonate; this may be made into a paste with hydrogen peroxide and ammonia for application as a "pack." Instead of hydrogen peroxide, sodium perborate may be used as part of the original "white henna", in which case the directions for use should call for the addition of water instead of hydrogen peroxide.

Chapter 12

SUNTAN PREPARATIONS

UNDER THE OPTIMAL CONDITIONS for sunburn, only 0.2 per cent of the total solar radiation is erythemogenic; its intensity depends primarily upon the sun's altitude, i.e., its variation with the seasons and with the daylight hours. The most intense erythemal radiation occurs in summer between the hours of 11 A.M. and 2 P.M.

A factor of considerable importance is the relationship between direct and scattered radiation. Scattering of light is caused by molecules of the atmosphere. The extent to which it occurs depends upon the wave length; thus in the case of visible radiation, the shorter-wave blue is scattered more than the longer-wave yellow or red. In the case of the ultraviolet component, in the range of 3200 Angstrom or less, the intensities of the direct and the scattered radiations are about equal. On an overcast day, the scattered, i.e., the indirect radiation may be even more intense than the direct one; this explains the frequent occurrence of sunburn on overcast days when least expected by the unwary sun bather.

The several skin layers are penetrated by radiation of different wave lengths which produce different effects. Thus radiant energy of 2000 to 2500 Angstrom penetrates only the horny layer while that of 2500 to 2800 Angstrom penetrates the granular cell layer, as well. However, radiation of 2800 to 3200 Angstrom penetrates also the *rete vasculosum* reaching into the papillary layer. The latter two ranges are both erythemogenic and pigmentogenic in action. The longer waves of 3200 to 3900 Angstrom which reach into the derma, are pigmentogenic but produce only little erythema, while those of 3900 to 14,000 Angstrom have a heating action which causes hyperemia in the subcutaneous tissue; this is entirely different from the erythema which is of a congestive character. Solar erythema originates mostly in the derma, and especially in the papillary layer, as a result of dilatation of blood vessels in this area. Pigment formation occurs mostly in the cylindrical cell layer.

The following table correlates the wavelengths of ultraviolet radiation with their relative erythemal effectiveness for the untanned skin:

Wavelength	*Erythemal Effectiveness*	*Wavelength*	*Erythemal Effectiveness*
2399	95	2804	6
2482	90	2894	25
2537	80	2925	70
2576	70	2967	100
2654	30	3024	50
2675	20	3132	2
2700	15	3342	0.4
2760	5	3663	0.12

Beginning with the wavelength of 2399 Angstrom, which shows the effectiveness of 95, there is first a steady decrease until the wavelength of 2804 Angstrom is reached, followed by an increase to a maximum at 2967 Angstrom. At 3024 Angstrom the erythemal effectiveness is one-half that at 2967; still longer waves show a steep decrease.

Tanning follows upon erythema which stimulates its development. Melanin is formed first in the basal layer where, of course, it cannot immediately protect the prickle cells which are located above it; only later, as the melanin granules migrate outward, does the pigmentation exert its protective action against erythemal radiation.

Melanin is formed in the melanocytes (melanoblasts) where tyrosine is transformed first into dihydroxyphenyl alanine (DOPA), and ultimately into melanin, by the action of tyrosinase. This reaction is activated by the coenzyme cuproprotein; radiation (ultraviolet, also roentgen and thorium X) is a factor which additionally influences this enzymatic process, as confirmed with the aid of C^{14} tagged tyrosine. The tyrosin-tyrosinase system exists in the normal skin of both the white and the colored races.

As to the tanning action of the longer-wave radiation, i.e., outside of the normal erythemal range, both an erythemal and a tanning activity is shown in the range of 3300 to 4200 Angstrom, with a strong maximum at 3800 and two weaker maxima at 3600 and 4080 Angstrom. The radiation around 3650 Angstrom produces immediate tanning; several hundred times as much energy is required of such radiation as of that of 2967 Angstrom to produce a minimum perceptible erythema.

The tanning action of radiant energy of longer waves probably depends upon the darkening of preformed propigment. This conclusion derives from the fact that tanning by long-wave ultraviolet does not occur in the absence of oxygen, whereas true erythema and "melanization" of the skin do not seem to be affected under similar conditions. Histological examination reveals that inflammatory reactions, such as occur in the wake of shortwave irradiation, are not found after irradiation with wavelengths over 3200 Angstrom. Incidentally, a portion of tan of solar origin may be due to a darkening of preformed pigment (possibly a leucoform), because of the greater proportion in the solar radiation of the range of 3200 to 4200 Angstrom than of wavelengths shorter than 3200 Angstrom; this may play a role particularly when the sun is not in the zenith, e.g., later in the afternoon or earlier in the morning.

While irradiation with wavelengths longer than 3200 Angstrom causes an immediate tanning response, in the case of wavelengths shorter than 3200 Angstrom the tanning response occurs after the erythema has begun to subside; actually, the maximum of pigmentation almost coincides with the disappearance of erythema. Whereas the erythemal maximum is produced about ten hours after irradiation, the maximum development of pigmentation occurs some 100 hours, i.e., four days later. It should be stressed that pigmentation obtained solely through exposure to long-wave ultraviolet furnishes little or no immediate protection against the erythemogenic short-wave ultraviolet.

Solar irradiation brings about a thickening of the horny layer of the epidermis; since the *stratum corneum* is rather opaque to ultraviolet light, a moderate increase in its thickness will provide a marked increase in its opacity to erythemal radiation. Melanin also contributes toward absorption of the ultraviolet light, but only in the later stages when the pigment granules which are formed originally in the basal layer have migrated toward the horny layer.

As a rule, it is the mission of a sunburn preventive either to scatter the sunlight effectively, or to absorb a substantial portion of its erythemogenic radiation.

Opaque materials applied either in dry form, or incorporated in suitable vehicles, will serve as light-scattering agents; talc, kaolin, zinc oxide, calcium carbonate, magnesium oxide, and titanium dioxide belong in this class.

The true "sunscreens" which operate by absorption of the erythemal ultraviolet radiation represent a comparatively recent development. The first such cosmetic product appears to have been introduced in the United States in 1928; it contained, as its active agent, a combination of benzyl cinnamate with benzyl salicylate in an emulsion vehicle. Since then the number of sunburn preventives and related preparations has increased enormously.

An acceptable screening agent must satisfy a number of requirements. In addition to a capacity for absorbing most of the erythemogenic radiation, it must show no photolability; in other words, under the influence of light it must not undergo any intramolecular changes, nor participate in any chemical reactions (e.g., oxidation) that would affect its absorptive capacity. This is why the physical determination of the ultraviolet absorption spectrum of a given substance intended as a sunscreen will not supply any definitive information as to its stability under practical conditions of exposure which might, conceivably, reduce its effectiveness after a longer or shorter period of time, sometimes to the point of complete ineffectiveness. Of course, a sunscreen must be neither toxic nor irritant; nor must it have a record of a sensitizing potential. It must be nonvolatile, and it must retain its activity in the presence of perspiration.

As a general rule, the screening material is not applied in its pure state, but incorporated in a suitable vehicle which may be aqueous, alcoholic, fatty, or a combination of those mentioned, i.e., in the form of a solution, emulsion, a cream, etc. Obviously, the requirements as to skin tolerance and freedom from any undesirable features apply to the vehicle with the same force as to the protective principle. In view of the prevalent vogue of "oiling" the skin prior to sunning, it is deemed pertinent to consider the information given in the following table:

Ultraviolet Absorption of Several Oils

	Per Cent		Per Cent
White mineral oil	0	Poppyseed oil	23
Coconut oil	23	Cottonseed oil	26
Peanut oil	24	Sesame oil	39
Olive oil	23		

which shows that several oils of vegetable origin have but a limited capacity for absorption of the erythemal radiation. Sesame oil is the most effective in this regard. By contrast, mineral oil appears to be totally devoid of any absorptive capacity. The latter fact is significant in view of the extensive use on beaches of certain "baby oils" of mineral oil character, probably based on their reputed "blandness"; it is obvious that such oils can supply hardly any protection against sunburn.

As emphasized before, it is not the proper purpose of a sunscreen completely to prevent the sun's ultraviolet radiation from reaching the skin. Rather, it should reduce its intensity sufficiently so as to enable the skin to build up its own protection against further exposure, primarily by the thickening of the *stratum corneum*, and secondarily by tanning.

Over a period of time, a considerable number of chemicals have become known which are suitable for use as sunscreens. Their selection for any particular formulation depends upon a number of factors among which are screening efficiency, solubility (or emulsifiability), and economy. More efficient sunscreens permit the use of lower concentrations which, therefore, may be more economical than the required higher concentrations of less expensive but also less effective materials.

The literature on sunburn prevention refers to numerous substances with "screening" action of which the following is a partial listing:

p-Aminobenzoic acid, its salts and its derivatives (ethyl, isobutyl, and glyceryl esters; *p*-dimethylaminobenzoic acid and esters).

Anthranilates (i.e., *o*-aminobenzoates; methyl, menthyl, phenyl, benzyl, phenylethyl, linalyl, terpinyl, and cyclohexenyl esters).

Salicylates (amyl, phenyl, benzyl, menthyl, glyceryl, 2-ethylhexyl and dipropyleneglycol esters).

Cinnamic acid derivatives (menthyl and benzyl esters; 2-ethoxyethyl *p*-methoxycinnamate; *o*-phenyl cinnamonitrile; butyl cinnamoyl pyruvate).

Dihydroxycinnamic acid derivatives (umbelliferone, methylumbelliferone, methylaceto-umbelliferone).

Trihydroxycinnamic acid derivatives (esculetin, methylesculetin, daphnetin, and the glucosides, esculin and daphnin).

Benzophenone derivatives (2,4-dihydroxybenzophenone).

Hydrocarbons (diphenylbutadiene, stilbene).

Dibenzalacetone and benzalacetophenone.

Naphtholsulfonates (sodium salts of 2-naphthol-3,6-disulfonic and 2-naphthol-6,8-disulfonic acids).

Dihydroxy-naphthoic acid and its salts.

o- and *p*-Hydroxybiphenyldisulfonates.

Coumarin derivatives (7-hydroxy, 7-methyl, 3-phenyl).

Diazoles and triazoles (2-acetyl-3-bromoindazole, phenyl benzoxazole, methyl naphthoxazole, various alkyl aryl benzothiazole and benzotriazole derivatives).

Quinine salts (bisulfate, sulfate, chloride, oleate, and tannate).

Quinoline derivatives (8-hydroxyquinoline salts, 2-phenyl-quinoline).

Uric and violuric acids.

Tannic acid and its derivatives (e.g., hexaethylether).

(Butyl carbityl) (6-propyl piperonyl) ether.

2,4-Dibenzoyl resorcinol.

Hydroquinone.

Isomerism plays an important role in determining absorptive capacity for erythemal radiation. Thus, the *para*-isomer of aminobenzoic acid is superior in this respect to both the *ortho*- and *meta*-isomers; by contrast, ortho-hydroxybenzoic acid (salicylic acid) has a comparatively high absorption value while *para*-hydroxybenzoic acid has practically none.

A comparatively simple and rapid method of evaluating the relative absorption capacity of a number of sunscreens is based upon the determination of the optical density of their 0.1 per cent solutions in an 0.1 mm. silica cell at 3080 Angstrom, which is at the peak of the "sunburn curve." By reducing all readings to those of 1 per cent solutions, one obtains a series of "sunscreen indices" as shown in the following table:

Compound	*Sunscreen Index*
Ethyl *p*-dimethylaminobenzoate	14.80
Ethyl *p*-aminobenzoate	9.60
Isobutyl *p*-aminobenzoate	9.20
p-Aminobenzoic acid	7.40
Digalloyl trioleate	2.30
Ethyl gallate	1.40
Lauryl gallate	0.85
Salicylic acid	4.30
Methyl salicylate	4.00
Salicylamide	3.90
Sodium salicylate	2.40
Salicyl aldehyde	2.20
Dipropyleneglycol salicylate	1.90
p-Aminosalicylic acid	1.90
Methyl umbelliferone	7.70
Umbelliferone acetic acid	6.00

This table indicates that the esters of *p*-aminobenzoic acid yield the most effective sunscreens; the ethyl ester of *p*-dimethyl-aminobenzoic acid appears to be more effective than either the ethyl or the isobutyl ester of *p*-aminobenzoic acid. In the series of salicylic acid derivatives, the free acid is superior to both the methyl ester and the sodium salt. It should be noted, however, that some sunburn preventives containing derivatives of *p*-aminobenzoic acid tend to discolor light fabrics upon exposure to sunlight; the salicylic esters seem to be free from this drawback.

The ultraviolet absorption characteristics of the sun screens can be affected by different excipients and additives to a minor or major degree. Sometimes the ambient pH will have a profound effect. Thus, in the case of *p*-aminobenzoic acid, a change from pH of 3.7 to one of 9.2 (as produced by dissolving this compound in a sodium borate solution which signifies the conversion of the free acid to its sodium salt) shifts the absorption curve to the lower wavelengths, thereby all but destroying its sunscreen character.

The following formulas indicate some of the formulation possibilities:

Suntan Oil

	Per Cent
2-Ethyl hexyl salicylate	5.0
Sesame oil	40.0
Mineral oil	55.0
Antioxidant	q.s.

Suntan Lotion (Alcoholic)

	Per Cent
Menthyl anthranilate	5.0
Propyleneglycol ricinoleate	10.0
Glycerol	10.0
Alcohol	65.0
Water	10.0
Antioxidant	q.s

Suntan Cream (Liquid Emulsion)

	Per Cent
Glyceryl *p*-aminobenzoate	3.0
Mineral oil	25.0
Sorbitan monostearate (Arlacel 60)	4.0
Polyoxyethylene sorbitan monostearate (Tween 60)	6.0
Water	62.0
Preservative	q.s.

As in the case of numerous other chemicals applied externally, so also in that of sunburn preventives, individual cases of hypersensitivity have been encountered. Thus a case of allergic eczematous dermatitis has been caused by an ester of *p*-amino-benzoic acid, but sensitization by this substance was preceded by one to benzocaine and to a sulfonamide (possibly sulfaguanidine); hypersensitivity to aniline, aminoazobenzene, and paraphenylenediamine was also present. Accordingly, such a case of "cross-sensitization" indicates the possibility of allergic dermatitis from a sunscreen of the *p*-amino-benzoate class in those individuals who are hypersensitive to para-phenylenediamine, to aniline dyes, to sulfonamides, or to local anesthetics based upon the aniline structure.

In the recent past, a new tanning agent based upon dihydroxyacetone, has received wide publicity. This chemical, with the formula HOH_2CCOCH_2OH, when applied in a dilute solution to the skin, produces its gradual darkening which is accelerated by exposure to sunlight. (Arginine appears to be involved primarily in this reaction.) However, the pigment thus formed does not minimize the hazard of a sunburn. When employed for the purpose stated, dihydroxyacetone does not seem, at this time, to create any toxicological or sensitization problems in spite of prolonged usage.

To the extent that a given product is represented as a preventive or a treatment for sunburn, it is a "drug" within the meaning of this term as defined by the Federal Food, Drug, and Cosmetic Act, and must be labeled accordingly. Among other things, the label of a drug product is required to state the active ingredient or ingredients to which the prophylactic or therapeutic effect is attributed. Thus, a sunburn preparation may be both a "cosmetic" and a "drug."

However, if a product is represented merely as a means of acquiring a tan, it may be labeled as a "cosmetic" only; relevant provisions of the Act do not require a statement of the active ingredient for this type of representation.

It may be added here that oral ingestion of 8-methoxypsoralen, a drug used in the treatment of vitiligo, has been employed as a potentiating aid to suntanning because of its capacity to increase the skin's tolerance for sunlight, and to intensify its pigmentation (as compared with that of controls). However the question of safety of unsupervised routine use of this drug over a period of days or weeks has not been settled, particularly with respect to individuals manifesting gastrointestinal or hepatic dysfunction.

As a factor in retarding the *skin's aging,* protection against the ultraviolet portion of the sun's spectrum has acquired considerable importance in the recent past. This is derived from the observed damage to cutaneous tissue following upon extensive exposure to sunlight. Such an effect may express itself, among other things, in a degeneration of collagen, irregular pigmentation, and loss of elasticity; the visible results are dryness, wrinkling, sallowness. By contrast, those portions of the skin which are shaded by clothing do not display this aging syndrome; relevant is the fact that many elderly Negroes look younger than their age, owing to the protection of their skin against sunlight-promoted aging by its relatively intensive pigmentation.

With this as a premise, it has been suggested that the addition of sunscreening agents to cosmetics for routine daytime use (foundation creams, also hand creams and lotions) should retard the visible onset of the appearance of aging symptoms, provided that the use of such cosmetics is started early enough, and that it is continued through adolescence and maturity.

Chapter 13

PERFUMES, TOILET WATERS AND COLOGNES

WITH A FEW EXCEPTIONS, every cosmetic preparation is scented. Perfume is also used independently, i.e., for its fragrance alone.

Perfuming of cosmetic preparations, be they creams, lotions, face powders, lipsticks or others, calls for considerable circumspection; in addition to acceptability as a fragrance, the perfume chosen must satisfy a number of technical requirements, e.g., as to stability, persistence, non-interference with the cosmetic formula, and freedom from irritancy or sensitization, to mention but a few.

The modern perfumer has at his disposal literally thousands of materials from which to blend a perfume; actually, a scent may contain from one to fifty or more components.

There are two broad categories of perfume materials, *viz.*, the natural and the synthetic; there is some overlapping between these two groups in that some naturally occurring odoriferous substances can be, or are being produced synthetically.

The natural materials originate with vegetable or animal sources.

The vegetable or plant materials comprise the floral oils, the essential oils and the group of gums, resins and balsams.

Floral Oils. Mostly of foreign origin, these oils are obtained, as a rule, either by "enfleurage" or by solvent extraction. In enfleurage, the freshly picked flower petals are spread on framed glass panels coated with highly purified animal fats (lard, tallow). When stacked, these frames form a series of airtight chambers in which the petals "exhale" their perfume to be absorbed by the fat. Every twenty-four to forty-eight hours, the frames are disassembled, the exhausted floral material is removed and a new charge is introduced. The process is repeated until the fat is saturated with the floral oil, whereupon it is scraped off and replaced by fresh fat. The saturated fat is extracted with alcohol which dissolves the floral oil, but leaves the fat behind. The residue left upon evaporation of the alcohol is the floral "absolute."

The process of enfleurage is applied, e.g., in the production of oil of jasmin, one of the most versatile floral oils, which is present in almost any fine perfume. Direct extraction of the floral material with suitable volatile solvents is employed, e.g., with some varieties of French rose, but not with Bulgarian rose which yields the famous "attar" of roses; here the initial separation of the rose oil is effected by steam distillation.

Essential Oils. This is a large group of odorous materials obtained from different plants, either by steam distillation or by pressure. The former process is applied to the leaves or needles, roots, also to certain woods, the latter to the peels of citrus fruits. Among the most common or better known essential oils are those of peppermint, spearmint, pine needles, vetiver, clove, orange and bergamot, but there are many others.

Gums, Resins and Balsams. These materials usually represent tree exudates. Examples are gum styrax, labdanum, myrrh, balsam Peru. There are numerous natural materials in this category.

Animal Perfume Materials. Of the four substances from animal sources which play an important role in perfumery, ambergris, represents a morbid secretion from the sperm whale, civet is obtained from the Abyssinian civet cat (contained in a pouch near its genitals), musk is furnished by the musk deer (held in a sac under the skin of the abdomen), and castoreum comes from the beaver (and represents the dried secretion of the perineal glands).

All modern fragrances contain "isolates" and "synthetics." The former are separated from the plant oils whose primary odorous constituents they represent. Sometimes the same isolate may be obtained from several different plant oils. Thus, linalool occurs in the oils of linaloe seed, petitgrain, rosewood and others; but since it cannot be isolated in an entirely pure form, the source of its origin affects its odor character and, therefore, its appeal to the perfumer. Other examples of commonly used isolates are citral (from lemon grass oil) and geraniol (from citronella oil).

By reacting some isolates with suitable chemicals, new odorous compounds are formed which have no natural counterparts. Thus geraniol may be esterified with propionic acid to yield geranyl propionate, with an odor quality related to, but not identical with that of geraniol.

Finally, there are the true "synthetics," derived from nonphysiological sources, such as coal tar, petroleum and others. Some of these synthetics may have their counterparts in nature (e.g., methyl salicylate in wintergreen oil), while others are strictly artificial products without any natural counterparts or relatives. Examples of the latter category are furnished by the important synthetic musks; "musk xylene" is 2,4,6-trinitro-1,3-dimethyl-5-*tert*butyl benzene:

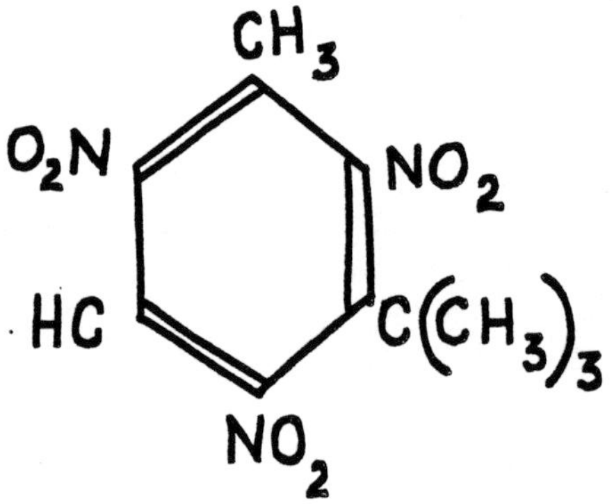

CH_3

O_2N NO_2

HC $C(CH_3)_3$

NO_2

Perfumes are generally understood to be alcoholic solutions containing from 15 to 25 per cent of the perfume concentrate; the latter usually consists of a blend of floral oils, synthetics and "fixatives" derived from animal products plus resins and balsams. While the floral oils contribute quality to the perfume, it is entirely feasible to construct a perfume without them. Thus simple fragrances of a rose or a carnation character, respectively, could be produced from the following seven ingredients, but varying their proportions, as follows:

	"Rose"	*"Carnation"*
Geraniol	50.0	10.0
Phenyl ethyl alcohol	35.0	25.0
Terpineol	5.0	2.0
Ionone	3.0	4.0
Benzyl acetate	3.0	3.0
Eugenol	2.0	55.0
Amyl cinnamic aldehyde	2.0	1.0

Of course, as has been emphasized before, modern perfumes are highly complex mixtures, often consisting of a great number (of the order of fifty or more) of components from the several sources referred to.

Toilet waters are alcoholic solutions containing lower proportions (e.g., 3 to 5 per cent) of the perfume concentrate. Colognes and toilet waters mean the same today; however, *Eau de Cologne* represents a special type of product (available in various modifications) whose odorous principle is based upon a blend of the oils of lemon, bergamot and rosemary.

There are a number of published reports involving both synthetic and natural perfume materials in eczematous dermatitis; among them are linalool, citronellol, heliotropin, vanillin, eugenol, isoeugenol, methyl heptine carbonate, benzylidene acetone, also the essential oils of cloves, bergamot, lemon and cassia, and the floral oils of neroli and lavender. Some of these reports merit brief discussion for their instructive value.

Methyl heptine carbonate is a synthetic perfume material of the formula $H_3C(CH_2)_4C \equiv COOCH_3$. It was involved in a case of lipstick dermatitis attributed to the use of the perfume with which the lipstick was scented. It was found to be capable of producing specific sensitivity in guinea pigs when applied repeatedly either by intracutaneous injection of its solution in olive oil, or by inunction of the unbroken skin. This effect has been ascribed by the investigators to its reaction with a protein and the resultant creation of a specific antigen.

While the above is an example of singular sensitization specificity, a group specificity is observed in the case of chemically related substances. Thus, in an established case of sensitivity to citronella oil, a cutaneous reaction was produced also by lemon oil; tests with some of the constituents of these oils elicited a strong positive response with citronellol, and a weaker one with citral and geraniol.

Sunlight plays a role in the Berlock dermatitis of Eau de Cologne in which the inciting agent appears to be bergamot oil. According to a recent idea, the furocoumarins present in a variety of natural essential oils (including oil of bergamot) are responsible for the hyperpigmentation which is characteristic of this type of photodermatitis.

Balsams and resins, too, are involved in sensitization reactions, as observed in the cases of balsam Peru, balsam Tolu, gum benzoin and gum styrax. The coniferyl alcohol esters present in these substances of rather complex composition appear to be the most important allergens. Other related materials with a sensitization potential are opopanax and copaiba balsam.

For the sake of completeness mention should be made of the allergenic effect of inhaled perfume which is due to some offending volatile component of the perfume entering through the respiratory tract. In some instances, a purely nasal hypersensitiveness (as manifested by rhinorrhea) was observed, i.e., without any concomitant cutaneous response, while in other cases nasal and cutaneous reactions were found to run parallel.

At any rate it should be kept in mind that of the numerous categories of aromatics constituting the bulk of the perfume compositions there are aldehydes, ketones, phenols, amino- and nitrocompounds, unsaturated hydrocarbons and others characterized by reactive groups coupled with solubility properties which preclude any *a priori* idea as to freedom from irritant or sensitizing action, i.e., without an actual cutaneous test. Yet only little information is available as to the irritant or sensitizing potentials of individual perfume ingredients. Considering the size and diversity of the perfumer's armamentarium, and the complexity of most perfume formulas, it is readily understood why the identification of an allergenic agent, either natural or synthetic, in a finished perfume or in a perfumed cosmetic is a task of major proportions.

Chapter 14

HORMONE COSMETICS

ALTHOUGH THE SUBJECT of hormone cosmetics has been, and continues to be controversial in character, it is deemed desirable to deal with it within the framework of this lecture course for the sake of establishing the facts and the issues involved.

The original idea of allowing certain sexual steroids to act upon the skin derives from the postulate of an essential similarity in the atrophic appearance of the skin of aged and of hypogonad (or castrated) individuals. It was known that the therapy of hypogonad subjects with the appropriate sex hormones (i.e., estrogen in the case of females, and testosterone in that of males) would produce an improvement in the texture as well as in the color of the skin, ostensibly by overcoming the skin's inadequate content of these steroids. Accordingly, it seemed logical to inquire into the possibility of delaying or even reversing the syndrome of dermal senescence by topical hormone action, thereby avoiding untoward reactions within the body while achieving the desirable cosmetic "correction" of the senile skin.

What are some of the symptoms that characterize the atrophic senile (or hypogonad) skin? Compared with a young skin, the senile skin is thinner and paler, its pallor being due to a poorer capillary circulation. Its elasticity is lessened owing to a disarrangement and fragmentation of the elastic fibrils, and there is a dearth of tissue fluid in the collagen. The epidermal pegs are absent, and there is no evidence of proliferative activity in the basal cell layer.

Several investigators in both the dermatological and endocrinological fields claim that as a result of topical application of different estrogenic substances for an adequate period of time, some or all of these atrophic symptoms tend to retrogress, as supported by histological evidence. The maximum effect is obtained after thirty to forty days from the inception of the treatment; upon its discontinuance the skin returns gradually to its original atrophic condition.

To produce this kind of reaction, the estrogenic substance must be absorbed percutaneously. It is known that estrus can be produced in experimental animals following application of an estrogen by inunction, but in an amount seven to ten times greater than required to elicit the same effect following subcutaneous injection. On the other hand, from a correct dose of topically applied estrogen, a sufficiency can be absorbed into the skin to produce the desired cutaneous effects, but without systemic action; in this case, any quantity which might have been absorbed into the system is too small to affect the normal level of endogenous estrogen to any significant degree.

Given a correct formulation which would permit gradual percutaneous absorption, the "natural" estrogens estrone and estradiol, and the synthetic stilbestrol yield comparable results. As a rule, a preparation equivalent in biological action to 10,000 International Units of estrone per ounce of excipient is deemed to be of the proper "strength" for cosmetic usage; by way of an added precaution against the risk of collateral action, not more than one ounce of such a product should be used up in two weeks. (i.e., not more than 20,000 I.U. per month).

One cosmetic hormone cream contains progesterone (in addition to estrone) for the sake of reactivation of retarded sebaceous function.

In the recent past, cosmetic effectiveness is being claimed for some steroids which are virtually free from any systemic hormonal capability (such as *cis*-testosterone, ethisterone, pregnenolone, alpha-estradiol, etc.). If confirmed, this would enable the formulator to employ substances possessed of a purely topical efficacy, and devoid of any hazard of systemic involvement even in the case of extensive misuse.

It may be added parenthetically that some years ago estrogenic hormone cosmetics were thought to be potentially carcinogenic. However, extensive use experience over a period of years militates against the validity of this idea. It should also be mentioned that the purely cosmetic effectiveness of estrogenic hormone preparations continues to be questioned by some investigators while being affirmed by others.

As to the formulation of a hormone cream, following is an illustrative formula of a "base" for such a cream:

	Per Cent
Mineral oil	30.0
Beeswax	15.0
Lanolin	15.0
Polyoxyethylene sorbitan monostearate (Tween 60)	7.5
Glyceryl monostearate	2.5
Sorbitol (Sorbo)	3.5
Water	26.5
Preservative	q.s.

To the above base a sufficiency of estrone or of other estrogenic substance is added to provide for a potency corresponding to that of 10,000 International Units of estrone per ounce of finished product, as ascertainable by biological assay.

Chapter 15

VITAMINS IN COSMETICS

WHILE NUMEROUS CREAMS AND LOTIONS (particularly those of the conditioning variety) contain vitamins, usually A and D, the effect of such vitamins upon the skin under the conditions of relevant cosmetic usage has not been determined with a degree of adequacy that would furnish a convincing rationale for their employment in formulation. A few facts have come to light, however, which might suggest further exploratory work in this area.

While there is experimental evidence that vitamin A is absorbed into and through the skin of rodents, it was thought at first that the human skin would not absorb this vitamin. However, several experiments performed in the recent past indicate that intact human skin, too, is penetrated by vitamin A; but only a small portion of it reaches the Malpighian layer whence conceivably a corrective effect is exerted upon faulty keratinization.

This kind of topical effect may be responsible for the observed improvement by a vitamin ointment in the condition of the senile skin, involving alleviation of dryness and scaliness; it has not been determined whether it depends upon the compensation of any existing cutaneous hypovitaminosisA, or upon some as yet undefined pharmacodynamic action of the vitamin following its topical application.

While vitamin D is absorbed through the skin (when applied in sufficient amounts) to produce an antirachitic effect in the case of vitamin D deficiency, neither the normal nor the senile skin appears to benefit cosmetically from its application. Similar considerations as to the absence of cosmetic (but not therapeutic) benefits hold true of the other fat soluble vitamins, *viz.*, E and K.

As to the water soluble vitamins, the addition to certain cosmetics of panthenol, the alcohol analog of pantothenic acid, is being advocated on the grounds that as a non-sensitizing aid to the healing of damaged tissue it could play a positive role in preparations applied to body areas which are subject to irritation, abrasion, excoriation and the like. Among the preparations which might be "improved" by the addition of panthenol are, e.g., the antiperspirants and the lipsticks, the former being applied to the axillary fossae which are subject to maceration and irritation produced not only by sweating but also by some antiperspirants, while the latter are used on lips which are subject to chapping, cracking, etc., through prolonged exposure to the elements (wind, sun), overheated rooms, and other deleterious ambient factors.

Although the vitamins B_2 (riboflavin) and B_6 (pyridoxine) appear to be absorbed by the skin when applied topically, they are not credited with any cosmetic efficacy. Niacinamide ointment is said to exhibit antipruritic, keratolytic and keratoplastic properties.

Chapter 16

BABY COSMETICS

THE SKIN of the adult differs more or less markedly from that of an infant, both physiologically and histologically; the latter is also more susceptible to irritation and infection. This is why special consideration must be given not only to the composition of skin care items intended to contact the skin of infants or newborn, but also to their manner and frequency of application.

There is no unanimity of pediatric opinion as to the type of cleanser that would be most suitable for use during the first few days of life. While some advocate skin cleansing with oil (with deferment of the full bath), others oppose the early use of oil on the grounds that it seals off the sebaceous and sweat ducts, thereby creating the risk of miliaria. Accordingly, cleansing with plain water and with only occasional use of a mild soap is deemed preferable. It is argued also that in the case of overcare, continuous removal of the skin's natural lipids either by emulsification with soap, or dissolution by oil, leads to asteatosis and eventually to chafing and fissuring which may predispose the skin to infection.

As the child grows older, the problem of proper cleansing in the diaper area acquires considerable significance. When urine is contaminated by bacteria present on the baby's skin, ammonia is generated owing to microbial decomposition of urea, according to:

$$CO(NH_2)_2 + 2H_2O \longrightarrow [(NH_4)_2CO_3] \longrightarrow 2NH_3 + H_2O + CO_2$$

(Although *B. ammoniagenes* has been assumed originally to be involved in this reaction, recent indications point to a causal participation of other microorganisms, notably *B. proteus, Ps. aeruginosa* and *Staph. aureus.*)

The characteristic dermatitis produced by ammonia from urinary urea is known as "diaper rash." This primary condition may be aggravated further by maceration of the skin in the presence of moisture, by friction with coarse-textured diaper material, or by irritant detergent or antiseptic residues remaining in improperly laundered or incompletely rinsed diapers.

The biological activity of ammonia producing microorganisms can be controlled by means of suitable bacteriostatic agents added to the final rinse for the laundered diapers. However, the use of potentially toxic or irritant chemicals (such as mercurials) should be avoided. Satisfactory inhibition of ammonia formation, accompanied by skin tolerance of the "sanitized" diapers is achieved by employing in the rinse the correct concentration of an acceptable antibacterial agent, e.g., one from the quaternary ammonium or synthetic phenolic classes.

While the application of oil to the skin of the newborn is controversial, as mentioned above, there is hardly any question as to the utility of light oils and oil emulsions for cleansing the diaper area. Moreover, the residual oil film may be expected to counteract chafing by maceration or friction, also to minimize skin contact with urine and ammonia. Where there still is any authoritative objection to the use of a baby oil on the grounds of a prolonged skin occlusion, the use of a good baby emulsion should overcome it, as a rule.

Following is an illustrative formula of a baby oil:

Baby Oil

	Per Cent
Mineral oil	80.0
Isopropyl myristate (palmitate)	15.0
Lanolin	5.0

and one of a baby lotion (non-ionic emulsion):

Baby Emulsion

	Per Cent
Mineral oil	35.0
Lanolin	5.0
Sorbitan monooleate (Arlacel 80)	2.0
Polyoxyethylene sorbitan monooleate (Tween 80)	5.0
Water	53.0
Preservative	q.s.

Antibacterial agents (hexachlorophene, chlorothymol, bithionol) may be added in judicious proportions. The presence of silicone will further counteract the risk of moisture-caused irritation.

Where a higher degree of emolliency is desired, baby creams fill such a need because of their lower water content.

The composition of *baby powders* corresponds in general to that of ordinary dusting powders. Pure talc will make a satisfactory baby powder; occasional preference is expressed for one of the starches (rice or corn starch) for this purpose because of their capacity for absorbing moisture. Since moist starch is subject to bacterial attack, baby powders based upon, or containing starch should be "medicated" with a suitable antiseptic agent designed to inhibit microbial activity.

Chapter 17

BATH COSMETICS

THE DIFFERENT PRODUCTS in this category do not all serve the same purpose although any particular product may serve two or more purposes. Thus depending upon their chemical character, *bath salts* may merely perfume the bath water, or they may also soften it. Bath salts which only scent (and sometimes tint) the water may be nothing more than rock salt (sodium chloride) with some perfume and color added. Bath salts based upon a mixture of sodium chloride with a sufficiency of trisodium phosphate will produce additionally a water softening effect, and the same is true of a sodium sesquicarbonate based product.

It should be noted that additives such as trisodium phosphate, sodium carbonate, borax, etc., produce an alkaline reaction to which an excessively dry or sensitive skin may respond unfavorably.

By combining a solid organic acid (such as tartaric) with a carbonate or bicarbonate in the dry state, one obtains effervescent bath salts; the effervescence is due to the liberation of carbon dioxide upon contact with the bath water.

Another bath cosmetic is the *bath oil,* of which there are two types, *viz.,* the insoluble and the "soluble" (emulsifiable). The former represents a solution of a perfume essence in a suitable oily vehicle; when added to the bath water, it collects on its surface as a fine film which emits the scent into the atmosphere, aided by the temperature of the warm bath. The "soluble" bath oil contains, as a carrier, usually a water-dispersible sulfated vegetable oil (e.g., sulfated castor oil) which may also contribute a measure of detergency and water softening action.

The popular *bubble baths* are produced in liquid as well as in solid forms. Their bubbling action depends upon the presence in the formula of a surfactant agent which causes a copious foam to develop under the impact of a jet of water. Sodium lauryl sulfate and sodium lauryl sulfoacetate are examples of suitable surfactants; sodium chloride or sodium tripolyphosphate may be employed as "fillers." The following formula will yield bubbling bath salts:

"Bubbling" Bath Salts

	Per Cent
Sodium lauryl sulfoacetate	50.0
Sodium tripolyphosphate	50.0

From 2 to 5 per cent perfume is added to the dry mixture. A "bubbling bath oil" (liquid bubble bath) might be composed as follows:

"Bubbling" Bath Oil

	Per Cent
Triethanolamine lauryl sulfate	25.0
Water	72.5
Perfume	2.5

Chapter 18

BLEACH AND FRECKLE CREAMS

THE PREPARATIONS TO BE REVIEWED under this heading are intended to lighten the natural skin pigmentation by chemical action "in depth", i.e., either by acting upon existing extracellular pigment, or by directly interfering with, and retarding, the mechanism of pigmentation.

As to the former principle, oxidizing agents such as zinc peroxide, have not been found to be particularly effective as skin bleaches. A procedure embodying the latter, more effective principle, is carried out most often with the aid of "insoluble" mercurials, such as ammoniated mercury, incorporated in a suitable ointment, or in an emulsified cream or lotion vehicle. The effect of the mercurial appears to depend upon its replacing the copper in tyrosinase, thereby inactivating the enzyme and impeding the first step in the process of melanogenesis. Moreover, as active enzymatic action ceases, any existing pigment is gradually removed with the desquamating corneum, accompanied by a progressive lightening of the skin shade.

Since intracutaneous penetration of the active principle is a condition of its effectiveness, its proportion must be kept sufficiently low so as to minimize the risk of any extensive systemic absorption. According to a ruling of the Food and Drug Administration, the presence of not more than 5 per cent of ammoniated mercury (or not more than 0.2 per cent of bichloride of mercury) is permissive provided that the labeling on the container includes a warning against the continued use of the product in the case of any developing irritation (also cautions against application to abraded or sunburned skin, or on large areas of the body).

Following is an illustrative formula of a bleaching mercurial ointment:

Bleaching Ointment

	Per Cent
Petrolatum	92.0
Ammoniated mercury	3.0
Bismuth subnitrate	5.0

The role of bismuth subnitrate in bleaching cosmetics appears to be more traditional than rational. There is no convincing evidence in support of the proposition that it counteracts any irritant tendency of the mercurial, or that it accelerates the bleaching process.

The formula of a "vanishing" type of a bleaching cream might read:

Bleaching Cream

	Per Cent
Stearic acid	20.0
Ammoniated mercury	4.0
Bismuth subnitrate	5.0
Triethanolamine	1.0
Propylene glycol	5.0
Water	65.0

A bleaching lotion might have the following formula:

Bleaching Lotion

	Per Cent
Stearic acid	6.0
Beeswax	1.0
Triethanolamine	1.0
Sorbitol (70%)	10.0
Bichloride of mercury	.2
Alcohol	10.0
Water	71.8

In spite of their greater tendency to drying out, the emulsified bleaching creams and lotions have the advantage of permitting a finer layer to be applied to the skin than do the thicker ointments; this will reduce, of course, the quantity of the mercurial available for absorption.

Within the more recent past, the skin bleaching action of the monobenzyl ether of hydroquinone (monobenzone) has become known although as yet no significant amounts of cosmetics bearing this chemical appear to have reached the public. No doubt the known high sensitization potential of monobenzone is a deterrent to its broader, unsupervised use. However, a newer bleaching cream contains hydroquinone as its active principle.

Chapter 19

SUMMARY NOTES ON CUTANEOUS REACTIONS FROM COSMETICS

CONSIDERING THE TREMENDOUS VARIETY of cosmetics and their virtually universal usage, the conclusion is justified that as a class they do not constitute a hazard. Available evidence indicates also that the comparatively infrequent untoward reactions to cosmetics are due predominantly to allergic eczematous sensitization rather than to primary irritation.

As to the former, it is accepted generally that such sensitization can be brought about by a simple chemical which, without being antigenic *per se,* has the capacity of combining with some body protein, or otherwise affecting its structure, so as to convert it to an antigen; as a result, an immunological reaction is initiated which produces sensitivity to this chemical.

That all or most persons do not become sensitized by exposure to a given potential sensitizer is due to the wide individual variation in the genetic predisposition to such sensitization. This means also that with a given genetic inertia as a constant, an intrinsically *potent* sensitizer might overcome such resistance, thereby eliciting a sensitizing response in a greater number of individuals than would be the case with a *weaker* sensitizer. Photodynamic sensitization results when the antigenic combination (as described above) has rendered the skin susceptible to some form of radiant energy.

Primary irritation appears to be a possibility in the case of a *depilatory agent.* Since its effect involves partial cleavage of the hair keratin, it is conceivable that, particularly upon an unnecessarily prolonged contact, it could attack the horny layer of the skin so as to render it permeable; the alkaline reaction (pH around 12) at which this type of cosmetic operates, would furnish a contributing factor. Actually, however, the depilatories appear to have a rather good safety record; outside of an occasional minor irritation, no significant injurious effects have been connected with their use.

Somewhat similar considerations apply to *cold waving agents* which perform also by reacting with hair keratin (to open the "cystine bond"). Here, too, no serious risks appear to be connected with the use of these agents; however, there are reports of dermatoses of the hands of beauty parlor operators which attribute this type of skin damage to prolonged and repeated contact with thioglycolate solutions.

A special position is held by alkali based *hair straighteners*. As might be expected, instances of primary irritation have occurred as a consequence of their use.

Although *deodorants and antiperspirants* are often grouped together, a distinction should be made between them on pharmacological grounds, in the context of this paragraph. A true deodorant, i.e., one devoid of the capacity to affect the flow of perspiration, may depend for its effect solely upon the presence of a bacteriostatic agent, such as hexachlorophene, in a suitable excipient. On the other hand, an antiperspirant is formulated usually with an astringent aluminum salt which generates an acid reaction in the presence of moisture, owing to hydrolysis; the ambient acidity is thought to counteract the multiplication of bacteria whereby the antiperspirant becomes a deodorant as well.

While deodorants understandably are quite bland in action, some antiperspirants are known to have produced instances of primary irritation, albeit of a mild degree, as a rule. Only under exceptional circumstances, e.g., when applied immediately after shaving, is an antiperspirant likely to give rise to a case of folliculitis by causing bacterial pathogens to be enclosed within the hair follicles.

In a different class are the granulomatous lesions (with a sarcoid architecture) observed in the axillae of some individuals using some (but not all) *zirconium* based deodorants. These lesions are of an allergic rather than of an irritant character in that they develop as a result of sensitization to an anionic form of zirconium (specifically, sodium zirconium lactate).

There are a number of cosmetic categories exhibiting a capacity for sensitization in varying degrees.

In the case of *oxidative hair dyes,* paraphenylenediamine (or one of the other chemicals of related structure) may react with the keratin of the skin (scalp) in the same (or in a similar) manner in which it combines initially with the hair keratin, thereby creating a typical allergenic agent. Reference is made in the text to the possibilities of cross-sensitization with respect to substances of related chemical configuration, and particularly certain topical anesthetics, PABA-derived sunburn preventives, and sulfa-drugs.

Neither the vegetable (henna) nor the metallic hair coloring agents (lead, silver compounds) appear to create hazards of primary irritation or sensitization.

The involvement of *nail polish* in allergic contact dermatitis has been reported on several occasions. The neck and the face are the most frequent sites of an erythematous reaction which is usually due to the "resin" component of the formula (such as the toluenesulfonamide or methacrylate resins, or, primarily, their monomers). The nail bed, too, can be affected, as has been found in the case of a "base coat" type of nail cosmetic; in spite of an occasionally severe reaction accompanied by pain and bleeding, the damage is subject to gradual, spontaneous repair when the use of the offending agent is discontinued. As a rule, nail polish *removers* are not involved in the causation of cutaneous reactions.

Although *lipsticks* are among the most widely used cosmetics, the incidence of cheilitis due to their use is very low. Most modern lipsticks contain a substantial proportion of pigments which by virtue of their opacity tend to counteract any photosensitizing potential of the dyes incorporated in the formula (and designed to achieve "permanence" of the lip stain). An ingredient of the perfume may be a factor in cheilitis, as has been reported for lipsticks scented with a rose type of fragrance containing methyl heptine carbonate as a component.

Perfumes, colognes and *toilet waters* are used in enormous quantities, yet the incidence of cutaneous reactions attributed to their use is very small. However, the kind of topical photosensitization which culminates in Berlock dermatitis, has gained some notoriety.

In connection with *suntan cosmetics,* mention was made in the text of reports of direct sensitization, as well as of allergic reactions triggered by prior sensitization with substances structurally (immunochemically) related to some "sunscreens" (such as hair dyes, anesthetics or sulfa-drugs).

Bleach and freckle preparations containing inorganic mercurials as active ingredients are potential irritants.

In the case of reported or observed cutaneous reactions to presumably bland cosmetic products, such as cleansing or conditioning creams, hand lotions and the like, the possibility of *preservatives* or *antioxidants,* in addition to *perfume,* being causally involved, should be kept in mind.

REFERENCES

Neither the format nor the purpose of this monograph appears to call for an elaborate bibliography on cosmetic chemistry or technology. For a comprehensive study of these subjects, or of any of their particular aspects, reference may be made to the compendium *Cosmetics: Science and Technology* edited by Sagarin, Goulden, Klarmann and Powers (Interscience Publ., New York 1957).

Nor is it deemed appropriate to furnish here a historically complete list of relevant dermatological publications. In view of the virtually continuous changes in the formulation of cosmetics many older observations and conclusions are rendered inapplicable to currently available products. This is why only a selected listing of more recent papers is given below:

Cleansing Agents

BETTLEY, R. F. and DONOGHUE, E.: The irritant effect of soap on the normal skin, *Brit. J. Dermat.* *72*:67, 1960.

BLANK, I. H., and COOLIDGE, M. H.: Degerming the cutaneous surface II. Hexachlorophene (G-11), *J. Invest. Dermat.* *15*:257, 1950.

BLANK, I. H., and SHAPPIRIO, E. B.: Water content of stratum corneum III. Effect of previous contact with aqueous solutions of soaps and detergents, *J. Invest. Dermat.* *25*:391, 1955.

BLANK, I. H., and GOULD, E.: Penetration of anionic surfactants into the skin. III. Penetration from buffered sodium laurate solutions, *J. Invest. Dermat.* *37*:485, 1961.

BLOHM, S. G.: Connection between skin-irritating and protein-denaturing effects of some surface-active agents, *Acta dermato-venereol.* *37*:209, 1957.

FERGUSON, E. H., and ROTHMAN, S.: Synthetic detergents and eczematous hand eruptions, *A.M.A. Arch Dermat.* *80*:300, 1959.

GROSS, F., and SCHAAF, F.: Verhalten der Haut gegen Fettsäuren mittlerer

Kettenlänge, *Hoppe-Seyler's Zeitschr. f. physiol. Chem 295*:119, 1953.

GROSS, P., BLADE, M. O., CHESTER, B. J. and SLOANE, M. B.: Dermatitis of housewives as variant of nummular eczema, *A.M.A. Arch. Dermat. and Syph. 70*:94, 1954.

HARROLD, S. P.: Denaturation of epidermal keratin by surface active agents, *J. Invest. Dermat. 32*:581, 1958.

JACOBI, O. and HEINRICH, H.: The acid mantle of the skin, *Proc. Sci. Sec. T.G.A. 21*:6, 1954.

JACOBI, O.: Testing the effect of soaps and detergents on live human skin, *Drug and Cosmetic Industry 81*:754, 1957.

JAMBOR, J. J. and SUSKIND, R. R.: An etiologic appraisal of hand dermatitis I. The role of soap and detergents as sensitizers, *J. Invest. Dermat. 24*: 379, 1955.

JOHNSON, S. A. M., KILE, R. I., KOOYMAN, D. J., WHITEHOUSE, H. S., and BROD, J. S.: Comparison of effects of soaps and synthetic detergents on hands of housewives, *Arch. Dermat. and Syph. 68*:643, 1953.

LAUBE, F.: Changes of pH, alkali resistance, alkali and acid neutralization of skin after various baths, *Dermatologica 112*:453, 1956.

LINFIELD, W. M., and CASELY, R. E.: Should bacteriostats be added to toilet soaps, *J. Soc. Cosm. Chem. 13*:81, 1962.

NEIS, G.: Über das Eindringen von Fettsäuren in die Haut (nachgewiesen mittels Autoradiographie), *Dermat. Wchnschr. 141*:467, 1960.

SCHNEIDER, W., and TRONNIER, H.: Untersuchungen über die Einwirkung von Schutzsalben und Waschmittteln auf die menschliche Haut unter Anwendung einer modifizierten Alkalineutralisationsprobe, *Berufsdermatosen 6*:1, 1958.

STUPEL, H. and SZAKALL, A.: *Die Wirkung von Waschmitteln auf die Haut*, Dr. Alfred Hüthig Verlag, Heidelberg, 1957.

SUSKIND, R. R.: Cutaneous effects of soaps and synthetic detergents, *J.A.M.A. 163*:943, 1957.

SWANSON, F.: Clinical evaluation of neutral detergent bar, *J.A.M.A.* 162: 459, 1956.

SZAKALL A.: Über die Funktion des Stratum corneum conjunctum der Haut, ihr Zusammenhang mit den Reizwirkungen, *Fette, Seifen, Anstrichmittel* 62:172, 1960.

SZAKALL, A., and SCHULZ, K. H.: Die Permeation von Fettalkohol-Sulfaten and Natriumseifen definierter Kettenlänge (C_8-C_{18}) in die menschliche Haut, ihr Zusammenhang mit den Reizwirkungen, *Fette, Seifen, Anstrichmittel 62*:172, 1960.

VAN SCOTT, E. J., and LYON, J. B.: A chemical measure of the effect of soaps and detergents on the skin, *J. Invest. Dermat. 21*:199, 1953.

WEIDMAN, A. I., and SAWICKY, H. H.: Nummular eczema, *A.M.A. Arch. Dermat. 73*:58, 1956.

Conditioning and Foundation Cosmetics

BARNETT, G.: Lanolin derivatives and modifications, *Drug and Cosm. Ind.* *80*:610, 1957; *83*:292, 1958.

BLANK, I. H.: Factors which influence the water content of the stratum corneum, *J. Invest. Dermat.* *18*:443, 1952.

BLANK, I. H.: Further observations on factors which influence the water content of the stratum corneum, *J. Invest. Dermat.* *21*:259, 1953.

BLANK, I. H.: Action of emollient creams and their additives, *J.A.M.A.* *164*:412, 1957.

ELLER, J. J., and WOLFF, S.: Permeability and absorptivity of the skin, *Arch. Dermat. and Syph.* *40*:900, 1939.

GAUL, L. E., and UNDERWOOD, G. B.: Relation of dew point and barometric pressure to chapping of normal skin, *J. Invest. Dermat.* *19*:9, 1952.

HERRMANN, W. A.: Barrier creams. A comparative investigation of the protective action of barrier creams with and without silicone oil, *Acta Dermato-Venereol.* *37*:276, 1957.

HJORTH, N., and TROLLE-LASSEN, C.: Skin reactions to preservatives in creams, *Am. Perf.* *77*:(1), 43, 1962.

RUSSELL, B. F.: Some aspects of the biology of the epidermis, *Brit. M. J.* *1*:815, 1962 (March 24).

SHELMIRE, J. B., Jr.: Influence of oil-in-water emulsions on hydration of keratin, *J. Invest. Dermat.* *26*:327, 1956.

STEIGLEDER, F., and RAAB, W.: Skin protection afforded by ointments, *J. Invest. Dermat.* *38*:129, 1962.

SULZBERGER, M. B., WARSHAW, T., and HERRMANN, F.: Studies of skin-hypersensitivity to lanolin, *J. Invest. Dermat.* *20*:33, 1953.

SZAKALL, A.: Über die Eigenschaften, Herkunft und physiologische Funktionen der die H-Ionenkonzentration bestimmenden Wirkstoffe in der verhornten Epidermis. *Arch. klin. exp. Dermat.* *201*:331, 1955.

TAJKOWSKI, E. G. and REILLY, I. H.: Silicones—properties and possible uses in cosmetics, *Proc. Sci. Sec. T.G.A.* No. 20, Dec., 1953.

Make-up

CALNAN, C. D.: Allergic sensitivity to eosin, *Acta Allergol.* *13*:493, 1959.

FRUMES, G. M., LEWIS, H. M. and HENSCHEL, E. J.: Disturbance of nails and nail beds produced by artificial fingernails, *J.A.M.A.* *149*:828, 1952.

PECK, S. M., and PALITZ, L. L.: Sensitization to facial tissues with urea-formaldehyde resin, *J.A.M.A.* *160*:1226, 1956.

REIN, C. R., and ROGIN, J. R.: Allergic eczematous reactions of nail bed due to "undercoats", *Arch. Dermat. and Syph.* *61*:971, 1950.

STRITZLER, C.: Dermatitis of the face caused by guanine in pearly nail lacquer, *A.M.A. Arch. Dermat.* *78*:252, 1958.

Antiperspirants and Deodorants

BAER, R. L., and LUDWIG, J. S.: Allergic eczematous sensitization to neomycin, *Ann. Allergy 10:*136, 1952.

BLANK, I. H., and DAWES, R. K.: Antibacterial activity of weak solutions of aluminum salts, *A.M.A. Arch. Dermat. 81:*565, 1960.

BLANK, I. H., MORELAND, M., and DAWES, R. K.: Activity of aluminum Salts, *Proc. Scient. Sec. T.G.A. 27:*24, 1957.

BLANK, I. H., JONES, J. L., and GOULD, E.: A study of the penetration of aluminum salts into excised human skin, *Proc. Scient. Sec. T.G.A. 29:*32, 1958.

EPSTEIN, S.: Dermal contact dermatitis from neomycin: observations on forty cases, *Ann. Allergy, 16:*268, 1958.

FERGUSON, E. H.: A note on axillary odor, *J. Invest. Dermat. 24:*567, 1955.

HERRMANN, F. and SULZBERGER, M. B.: Control of axillary sweating and body odor, *J.A.M.A. 167:*1115, 1958.

KLARMANN, E. G.: Certain chemical and bacteriological aspects of antiperspirants and deodorants, *Acta Dermato-Venereologica, 37:*59, 1957.

KUNO, Y.: *Human Perspiration*, Thomas, Springfield, 1956.

LIVINGOOD, C. S., NILASENA, S., KING, W. C., STEVENSON, R. A., and MULLIN, J. F.: Pyogenic infections treated with neomycin, *J.A.M.A. 148:*334, 1952.

LYON, I., and KLOTZ, I. M.: The interaction of epidermal protein with aluminum salts, *J. Pharmac. Assoc. 47:*509, 1958.

NELSON, C. T., and SULZBERGER, M. B.: Inclusion of antibiotics in cosmetic preparations, *J.A.M.A. 169:*1626, 1959.

PECK, S. M., and KANTOR, I.: Germicides versus antibiotics and chemotherapeutics in the control of resistant staphylococcal infections of the skin, *Proc. Scient. Sec. T.G.A. 29:*19, 1958.

PRIOR, J. T., and CRONK, G. A.: Pathological changes associated with aluminum and zirconium compounds, *A.M.A. Arch. Dermat. 80:*447, 1959.

QUIE, P. G., COLLIN, M. and CARDLE, J. B.: Neomycin resistant staphylococci, *Lancet*, July 16, 1960.

REYNOLDS, H., HILDEBRAND, J. F., LIVINGOOD, C. S., and FOSNAUGH, R. P.: Clinical features of contact dermatitis due to neomycin, *Arch. Dermat. 80:*455, 1959.

SCHEIMANN, L. G., KNOX, G., SHER, D. and ROTHMAN, S.: The Role of bacteria in the formation of free fatty acids on the human skin surface, *J. Invest. Dermat. 34:*171, 1960.

SHELLEY, W. B., HURLEY, H. J., and NICHOLS, A. C.: Axillary odor, *Arch. Dermat. and Syph. 68:*430, 1953.

SHELLEY, W. B., and HURLEY, H. J.: The allergic origin of zirconium deodorant granulomas, *Brit. J. Dermat. 70:*75, 1958.

SHELLEY, W. B., and COHN, M. N.: Effect of topically applied antibiotic agents on axillary odor, *J.A.M.A. 159:*1736, 1955.

SIDI, E., HINCKY, M., and LONGUEVILLE, R.: Cross-sensitization between neomycin and streptomycin, *J. Invest. Dermat. 30*:225, 1958.

STRAUSS, J. S., and KLIGMAN, A. M.: Bacteria responsible for apocrine odor, *J. Invest. Dermat. 27*:67, 1956.

SULZBERGER, M. B., ZAK, F. G., and HERRMANN, F.: Studies on sweating. On the mechanism of action of local antiperspirants, *A.M.A. Arch. Dermat. 60*:404, 1949.

WHEATLEY, V. R.: Biochemistry of sebum, *J. Soc. Cosm. Chem. 10*:206, 1959.

Hair Waving

LEHMAN, A. J.: Health aspects of common chemicals used in hair waving preparations, *J.A.M.A. 141*:842, 1949.

VOSS, J. G.: Skin sensitization by mercaptans of low molecular weight, *J. Invest. Dermat. 31*:275, 1958.

Epilation and Depilation

VESTAL, P. W.: Preoperative preparation of the skin with a depilatory cream and detergent, *Am. J. Surg. 3*:398, 1952.

Hair Dyes

BAER, R. L.: Examples of cross-sensitization in allergic eczematous dermatitis, *Arch. Dermat. and Syph. 58*:276, 1948.

GAUL, L. E.: Paraphenylenediamine sensitivity; comparative patch test reactiveness of the ortha, meta and para isomers, *J. Invest. Dermat. 35*:231, 1960.

FISHER, A. A., PELZIG, A., and KANOF, N. B.: Persistence of allergic eczematous sensitivity and cross-sensitivity patterns to paraphenylenediamine, *J. Invest. Dermat. 30*:9, 1958.

PECK, S. M.: Toxic and allergic complications of hair dyes, *J. Soc. Cosm. Chem. 5*:113, 1954.

REISS, F., GAHWYLER, M., and LUSTIG, B.: Sensitivity to hair dyes, *J. Allergy 28*:134, 1957.

SCHWARTZ, L., and BARBAN, C.: Paraphenylenediamine hair dyes, *Arch. Dermat. and Syph. 66*:233, 1952.

Suntan Preparations

BAER, R. L., and MELTZER, L.: Sensitization to monoglyceryl para-aminobenzoate, *J. Invest. Dermat. 11*:5, 1948; *12*:31, 1949.

BECKER, S. W., JR.: Methods of increasing skin pigmentation, *J. Soc. Cosm. Chem. 9*:80, 1958.

BECKER, S. W., JR.: Use and abuse of psoralens, *J.A.M.A. 173*:1483, 1960.

BLUM, H. F.: "Carcinogenesis by Ultraviolet Light" Princeton University Press, 1959; Photobiological research with particular reference to skin, *J.A.M.A. 173*:1353, 1960.

DANIELS, F., JR.: Physical factors in sun exposures, *Arch. Dermat. 85*:98, 1962.

DRAIZE, J. H.: Appraisal of the toxicity of sunscreen preparations, *Arch. Dermat. and Syph. 64*:585, 1951.

GOLDMAN, L., BARKOFF, J., BLANEY, D., NAKAI, T., and SUSKIND, R.: Investigative studies with the skin coloring agents dihydroxyacetone and glyoxal, *J. Invest. Dermat. 35*:161, 1960.

HAILEY, C. and BURKS, J. W.: Contact dermatitis from currently popular tanning agents, *J.A.M.A. 174*:2072, 1960.

JILLSON, O. F., and CURWEN, W. C.: Phototoxicity, photoallergy and photoskin tests, *A.M.A. Arch. Dermat. 80*:678, 1959.

KANOF, N. H.: Protection of the skin against the harmful effects of sunlight, *Arch. Dermat. and Syph. 74*:46, 1956.

KESTON, B. M.: The effects of sunlight on the skin, *J.A.M.A. 161*:1565, 1956.

KLARMANN, E. G., Sunburn and its control, *Drug and Cosm. Ind. 81*: 299, 454 (1957); Suntan Preparations, Chapter 8 in *Cosmetics-Science and Technology* ed. by Sagarin, Goulden, Klarmann and Powers, Interscience Publishers, Inc., New York 1957.

KLEIN, S. A.: The aging skin, *Geriatrics 14*:716, 1959.

KNOX, J. M., GUIN, J., and COCKERELL, E. G.: Benzophenones-ultraviolet light absorbing agents, *J. Invest. Dermat. 29*:435, 1957.

KNOX, J. M., COCKERELL, E. G., and FREEMAN, R. G.: Etiological factors and premature aging, *J.A.M.A. 719*:631, 1962.

KUMLER, W. D. and DANIELS, T. C.: Sunscreen compounds, *J. Am. Pharmac. Assoc.* (Sci. Ed.) *37*:474, 1948.

LORINCZ, A. L.: Physiological and pathological changes in skin from sunburn and suntan, *J.A.M.A. 173*:1227, 1960.

MCGOVERN, V. J., and MACKIE, B. S.: The mechanism of solar carcinogenesis: a study of the role of collagen degeneration of the dermis in the production of skin cancer, *A.M.A. Arch. Dermat. 78*:218, 1958.

MIESCHER, G.: Histology of reactions to light, *Dermatologica 115*:345, 1957.

ROTHMAN, S. and HENNINGSEN, A. B.: The sunburn protecting effect of para-aminobenzoate, *J. Invest. Dermat. 11*:5, 1948.

WITTGENSTEIN, E., and BERRY, H. K.: Reaction of dihydroxyacetone (DHA) with human skin callus and amino compounds, *J. Invest. Dermat. 36*:283, 1961.

WITTGENSTEIN, E., and GUEST, G. M.: Biochemical effects of dihydroxyacetone, *J. Invest. Dermat. 37*:421, 1961.

Perfumes, Toilet Waters and Colognes

FRIEDERICH, H. C., and WITJENS, P. H.: Zur Frage der Verträglichkeit synthetischer Duftstoffe an der Haut des Menschen, *Mediz. Kosm. 9*: 253, 1958.

IPPEN, H.: *Lichtschäden und Lichtschutz durch Kosmetika.* Hüthig-Verlag, Heidelberg, 1957.

IPPEN, H. and RUHRMANN, H.: Photodermatitis pigmentaria Freund durch Kölnisch Wasser-Stift, *Zeitschr. f. Haut-u. Geschlechtskr. 23:*230, 1957.

KLARMANN, E. G.: Perfume dermatitis, *Ann. Allergy. 16:*425, 1958.

Hormone Cosmetics

BEHRMAN, H. T.: Hormone creams and the facial skin. *J.A.M.A. 155*:119, 1954.

EIDELSBERG, J.: Estrogens in urine and cytology of vaginal smears after the use of an estrogenic cream, *J. Med. Sciences 214:*630, 1947.

GOLDBERG, M. B., and HARRIS, F. I.: Use of estrogen creams, *J.A.M.A. 150:*790, 1953.

GOLDZIEHER, M. A.: Hormones in cosmetics, Chapter 48 in *Cosmetics-Science and Technology* ed. by Sagarin, Goulden, Klarmann and Powers, Interscience Publishers, Inc., New York 1957.

GOLDZIEHER, M. A.: Estrogens, *J. Soc. Cosm. Chem.* Jan. 1961.

GOLDZIEHER, J. W., ROBERTS, I. S., RAWLS, W. B., and GOLDZIEHER, M. A. *A.M.A. Arch. Dermat. and Syph. 66:*304, 1952.

KARNAKY, K. J.: An investigation of possible gynecological changes resulting from the topical use of an estrogen-progesterone cream with special emphasis on vaginal epithelial cell height and pH, *Tri-State Med. J. 8:*6, 1960.

KLARMANN, E. G.: The cosmetic aspects of estrogenic hormones, *J. Soc. Cosm. Chem. 1:*406, 1949.

MASTERS, E. J.: The percutaneous absorption of estrogen, *Proc. Scient. Sec. T.G.A. 33:*26, 1960.

PECK, S. M. and KLARMANN, E. G.: Hormone cosmetics, *Practitioner, 173:* 159, 1954.

PECK, S. M., KLARMANN, E. G., and SPOOR, H. J.: Treatment of acne vulgaris with estrone, *Arch. Dermat. 70:*452, 1954.

SCHAAF, F.: Neue für die Hautpflege geeignete Wirkstoffe, *Med. Kosm. 7:*144, 1958.

SCHAAF, F., and GROSS, F.: Tierexperimentelle Untersuchungen über den Einfluss von Steroiden auf die Haut, *Arch. f. klin. u. exp. Dermat. 205:* 312, 1957.

SILSON, J. E.: Pregnenolone acetate—a dermatologically active steroid, *J. Soc. Cosm. Chem., 13*:129, 1962.

SPOOR, H. J.: Measurements of natural skin oil; influence of topically applied hormones upon its production, *Am. Pract. 11:*497, 1960.

STERNBERG, T. H., LE VAN, P., and WRIGHT, E. T.: The hydrating effects of pregnenolone acetate on the human skin, *Current Ther. Res. 3*:469, 1961.

Vitamins in Cosmetics

REISS, F., and CAMPBELL, M.: The effect of topical application of vitamin A with special reference to the senile skin, *Dermatologica 108:*121, 1954.

RUBIN, S. H.: Percutaneous absorption of vitamins, *J. Soc. Cosm. Chem. 11:*160, 1960.

STÜTTGEN, G., and KRAUSE, H.: Der Nachweis von Tritium-markiertem Vitamin A in den Schichten der Haut nach lokaler Applikation, *Der Hautarzt 10:*504, 1959.

Baby Cosmetics

FISHER, R. S., FREIMUTH, H. C., O'CONNOR, K. A., and JOHNS, V.: Boron absorption from borated talc. *J.A.M.A. 157:*503, 1955.

LATLIEF, M. A., GOLDSMITH, M. I., FRIEDL, J. L., and STUART, L. S.: Prevention of ammonia formation from urea by *Proteus mirabilis. J. Pediat. 39:*730, 1951. Sanitization of cotton fabrics. *Ibid. 40*:324, 1952.

LEIDER, M.: *Practical Pediatric Dermatology* (2nd Ed.), Mosby, St. Louis, 1961.

LIPSCHUTZ, A. and FISCHER, C. C.: Methylbenzethonium chloride in the care of skin of infants and children. *Am. J. Diseases Children. 89:*596, 1955.

PERLMAN, H. H., and LEUALLEN, E. E.: What the pediatrician should know about the newer ointment bases. *J. Pediat. 43:*578, 1953.

RAPP, G. W.: The etiology of urine diaper rash. *Arch. Pediat. 72:*113, 1955.

OSBORNE, E. D., ROSS, J. R., WRONG, N. M., MCKEE, W. C. and FRAUENBERGER, G. S.: Pediatric dermatology, *Pediatrics 10:*710, 1952.

Bleach and Freckle Creams

BECKER, S. W., JR., and SPENCER, M. C.: Evaluation of monobenzone, *J.A.M.A. 180*:279, 1962.

LERNER, A. B.: Effect of ions on melanin formation, *J. Invest. Dermat. 18*:47, 1952.

LERNER, A. B., and FITZPATRICK, T. B.: Treatment of melanin hyperpigmentation, *J.A.M.A. 152:*577, 1953.

Cutaneous Reactions from Cosmetics (General)

Assoc. of Food and Drug Officials of the U. S.: *Appraisal of the Safety of Chemicals in Foods, Drugs and Cosmetics.* 1959.

BEHRMAN, H. T.: Cosmetic reactions and the clinical dermatologist, *Drug and Cosm. Ind. 88:*172, 1961.

GREENBERG, L. A., and LESTER, D.: *Handbook of Cosmetic Materials,* Interscience, New York, 1954.

HJORTH, N.: Cosmetic allergy, *J. Soc. Cosm. Chem. 10:*96, 1959.

KLARMANN, E. G.: The open problem of biological activity in cosmetics, *J. Soc. Cosm. Chem. 13*:65, 1962.

MASTERS, E. J.: Allergies to cosmetic products, *N. Y. State J. Med. 60*: 1934, 1960.

NELSON, C. T.: Clinical appraisal of dermatoses due to cosmetics, *J.A.M.A. 163*:740, 1957.

REISS, F.: Cosmetic dermatitis; a survey of its incidence, *Dermatologica 116*:419, 1960.

ROSTENBERG, A., JR.: Cutaneous reactions from cosmetics, *J. Soc. Cosm. Chem. 11*:169, 1960.

ROSTENBERG, A., JR.: Methods for the appraisal of the safety of cosmetics, *Drug and Cosm. Ind. 88*:592, 1961.

SCHWARTZ, L.: Cosmetic and dermatitis, *Med. Times. 82*:541, 1954.

SCHWARTZ, L.: Twenty-two years' experience in the performance of 200,000 prophetic patch tests, *Southern Med. J. 53*:478, 1960.

SIDI, E., and BOURGEOIS-SPINASSE, J.: *Verträglichkeit von kosmetischen Präparaten*, Dr. Alfred Hüthig Verl., Heidelberg, 1957.

SWINNY, B.: Periorbital dermatitis, *Ann. Allergy. 9*:774, 1951.

SUBJECT INDEX